Science Notebook

Glencoe Science

New York Science

Grade 7

Consultant
Douglas Fisher, Ph.D.

New York, New York Columbus, Ohio Chicago, Illinois

About the Consultant

Douglas Fisher, Ph.D., is a Professor in the Department of Teacher Education at San Diego State University. He is the recipient of an International Reading Association Celebrate Literacy Award as well as a Christa McAuliffe award for Excellence in Teacher Education. He has published numerous articles on reading and literacy, differentiated instruction, and curriculum design as well as books, such as *Improving Adolescent Literacy: Strategies at Work* and *Responsive Curriculum Design in Secondary Schools: Meeting the Diverse Needs of Students.* He has taught a variety of courses in SDSU's teacher-credentialing program as well as graduate-level courses on English language development and literacy. He also has taught classes in English, writing, and literacy development to secondary school students.

The McGraw·Hill Companies

Send all inquiries to:
Glencoe/McGraw-Hill
8787 Orion Place
Columbus, Ohio 43240-4027

ISBN: 978-0-07-877869-8

MHID: 0-07-877869-7

Printed in the United States of America

8 9 MAL 12 11

Table of Contents

Table of Contents

Note-Taking Tips

Your notes are a reminder of what you learned in class. Taking good notes can help you succeed in science. These tips will help you take better notes.

- Be an active listener. Listen for important concepts. Pay attention to words, examples, and/or diagrams your teacher emphasizes.
- Write your notes as clearly and concisely as possible. The following symbols and abbreviations may be helpful in your note-taking.

Word or Phrase	Symbol or Abbreviation
for example	e.g.
such as	i.e.
with	w/
without	w/o

Word or Phrase	Symbol or Abbreviation
and	+
approximately	≈
therefore	∴
versus	vs

- Use a symbol such as a star (★) or an asterisk (*) to emphasis important concepts. Place a question mark (?) next to anything that you do not understand.
- Ask questions and participate in class discussion.
- Draw and label pictures or diagrams to help clarify a concept.

Note-Taking Don'ts

- **Don't** write every word. Concentrate on the main ideas and concepts.
- **Don't** use someone else's notes—they may not make sense.
- **Don't** doodle. It distracts you from listening actively.
- **Don't** lose focus or you will become lost in your note-taking.

Using Your Science Notebook

This note-taking guide is designed to help you succeed in learning science content. Each chapter includes:

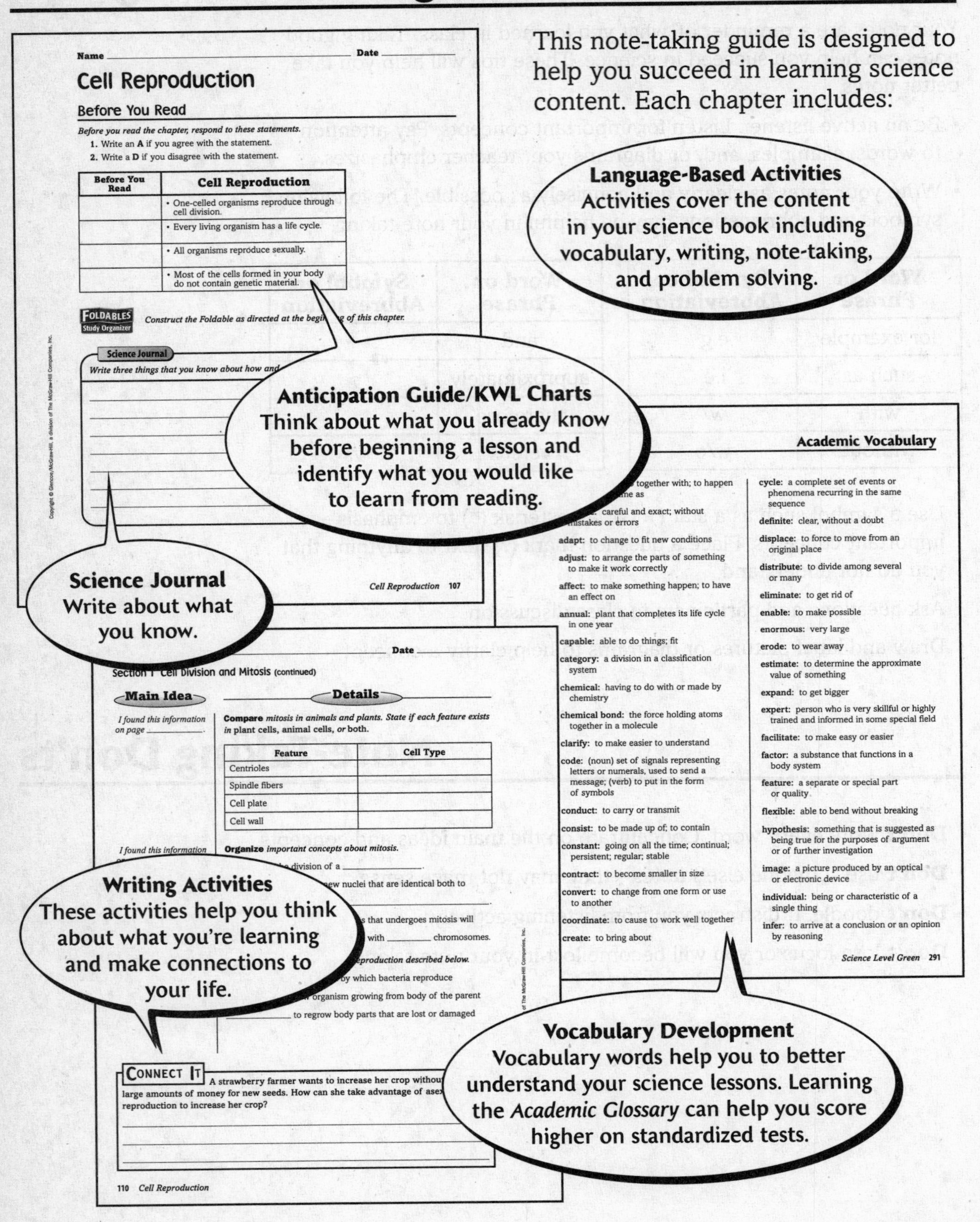

Name ______________________ Date __________

Section 1 Cell Division and Mitosis (continued)

Main Idea | **Details**

Why is cell division important?
I found this information on page ______.

Identify *the three reasons* cell division *is important.*

1. ______
2. ______
3. ______

The Cell Cycle
I found this information on page ______.

Summarize *information about* interphase in eukaryotic cells *in the following paragraph.*

Interphase is the ______ part of the cell cycle. During interphase, cells ______ and ______. During interphase, cells that are still dividing copy their ______ and prepare for ______. Cells no longer dividing are ______.

Mitosis
I found this information on page ______.

Sequence *the steps of* mitosis, *and write a short description of what takes place in each phase.*

1. ______
2. ______
3. ______

Chapter Wrap-Up
This brings the information together for you. Revisiting what you thought at the beginning of the chapter provides another opportunity for you to discuss what you have learned.

Note-Taking Based on the Cornell Two-Column Format
Practice effective note-taking through the use of graphic organizers, outlines, and written summaries.

Name ______________________ Date __________

Cell Reproduction Chapter Wrap-Up

Now that you have read the chapter, think about what you have learned and complete the table below. Compare your previous answers with these.

1. Write an **A** if you agree with the statement.
2. Write a **D** if you disagree with the statement.

Cell Reproduction	After You Read
• One-celled organisms reproduce through cell division.	
• Every living organism has a life cycle.	
• All organisms reproduce sexually.	
• Most of the cells formed in your body do not contain genetic material.	

Review
Use this checklist to help you study.

- ☐ Review the information you included in your Foldable.
- ☐ Study your *Science Notebook* on this chapter.
- ☐ Study the definitions of vocabulary words.
- ☐ Review daily homework assignments.
- ☐ Re-read the chapter and review the charts, graphs...
- ☐ Review the Self Check at the end of e...
- ☐ Look over the Chapter Review...

SUMMARIZE IT Li...

Review Checklist
This list helps you assess what you have learned and prepare for your chapter tests.

Name ______________________ Date __________

Section 2 Sexual Reproduction and Meiosis (continued)

Main Idea | **Details**

Sexual Reproduction
I found this information on page ______.

Compare *characteristics of* human diploid *and* haploid cells *in the table below. Give examples of each type of cell.*

Types of Human Cells		
	Diploid	Haploid
Number of chromosomes		
Process that produces them		
Examples		

Meiosis and Sex Cells
I found this information on page ______.

Model *the four stages of* meiosis I *in the spaces below. Use the figure in your book to help you.*

Meiosis I	
Prophase I	Metaphase I
Anaphase I	Telophase I

Graphic Organizers
A variety of visual organizers help you to analyze and summarize information and remember content.

Name ______________________________ Date __________

The Nature of Science

Before You Read

Before you read the chapter, respond to these statements.

1. Write an **A** if you agree with the statement.
2. Write a **D** if you disagree with the statement.

Before You Read	The Nature of Science
	• An important part of science is testing, or experimenting.
	• Technology is useful only in the situation for which it was designed.
	• People began studying weather in the 1800s.
	• Science can answer all of the questions that can be asked.

Construct the Foldable as directed at the beginning of this chapter.

Science Journal

How do you think scientists could learn more about a clump of stone that could be a small dinosaur heart?

Name ______________________ Date ______________

The Nature of Science

Section 1 Science All Around

AID M3.1a: Use appropriate scientific tools to solve problems about the natural world. **S1.2a:** Independently formulate a hypothesis. **Also covered:** AID S2.1c, S2.2b, S2.2c, S2.2d, IS 3.2, IPS 1.3, ED T1.1a

Scan *Section 1 of your book, reading all section titles and bold words. Then write three facts that you have learned about the nature of science and scientific investigation.*

1. ______________________

2. ______________________

3. ______________________

Review Vocabulary **Define** analyze *to show its scientific meaning.*

analyze ______________________

New Vocabulary *Write a sentence that contains both terms from each pair.*

hypothesis/control ______________________

scientific methods/ Earth science ______________________

variable/ independent variable ______________________

constant/ dependent variable ______________________

science/technology ______________________

Academic Vocabulary *Use a dictionary to define* outcome *to show its scientific meaning.*

outcome ______________________

Main Idea	Details
Mysteries and Problems *I found this information on page* ______.	**Summarize** *why it was important for scientists to solve the mystery of the tsunami that struck Japan, on January 27, 1700.* ______________________________ ______________________________ ______________________________ ______________________________
Scientific Methods *I found this information on page* ______.	**Sequence** *the* scientific methods *used to solve a scientific problem by completing the graphic organizer below.* [ ] ↓ Gather information. ↓ [ ] ↓ Test the hypothesis. ↓ [ ] ↓ [ ]
Science *I found this information on page* ______.	**Distinguish** *topics that Earth scientists study by listing specific topics identified in this section.* 1. ______ 7. ______ 2. ______ 8. ______ 3. ______ 9. ______ 4. ______ 10. ______ 5. ______ 11. ______ 6. ______ 12. ______

Name ______________________________ Date ______________

Main Idea **Details**

Working in the Lab

I found this information on page ______.

Define *the four types of factors in a science experiment. Identify and describe each of them below.*

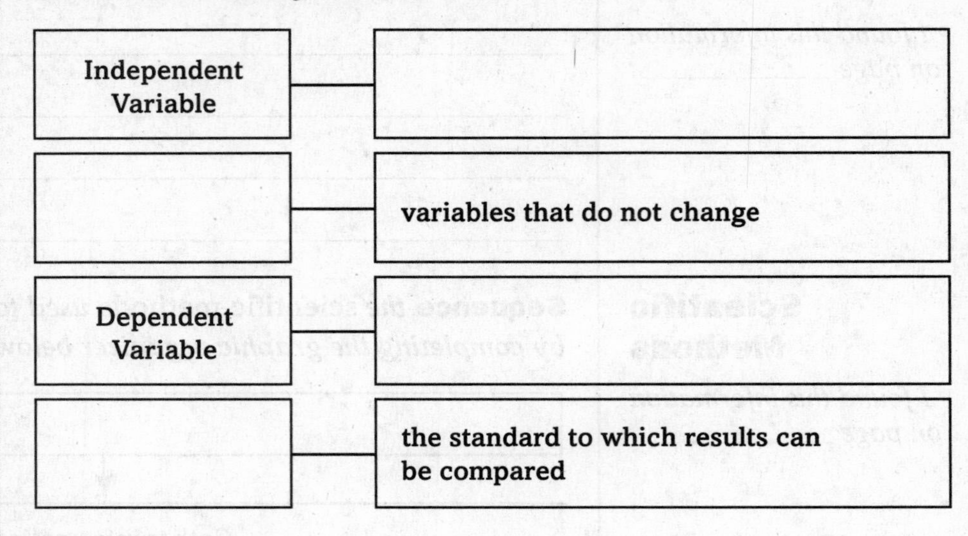

Technology

I found this information on page ______.

Summarize transferable technology *by defining the term. Then provide examples by filling out the graphic organizer below.*

Transferable technology is ____

____.

Radar and Sonar

originally developed for

are now used to study

SYNTHESIZE IT Identify three objects in your home or school that have *not* been affected by technology.

____

____

Name ______________________ Date ____________

The Nature of Science

Section 2 Scientific Enterprise

AID S3.2d: Formulate and defend explanations and conclusions as they relate to scientific phenomena. **S3.2g:** Suggest improvements and recommendations for further studying. **Also covered:** AID S3.1a, S3.2b

Skim *through Section 2 of your book. Write three questions that come to mind from reading the headings and examining the illustrations.*

1. ______________________

2. ______________________

3. ______________________

Review Vocabulary **Define** observation *to show its scientific meaning.*

observation ______________________

New Vocabulary *Use your book to define the following terms.*

scientific theory ______________________

scientific law ______________________

ethics ______________________

bias ______________________

Academic Vocabulary *Use a dictionary to define* objective *as an adjective.*

objective ______________________

Name ______________________ Date __________

Main Idea | **Details**

A Work in Progress

I found this information on page ______.

Summarize *how the manner in which people observe natural phenomena has changed over time.*

______

______

______

The History of Meteorology

I found this information on page ______.

Organize *types of weather information that can be measured. Complete the graphic organizer below.*

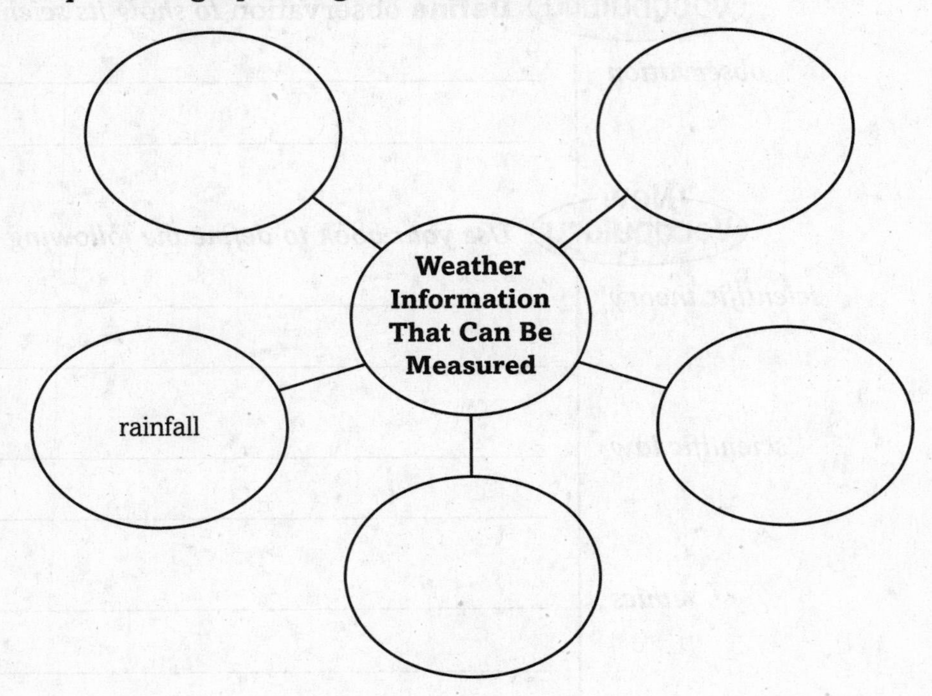

Continuing Research

I found this information on page ______.

Distinguish *between a* scientific theory *and a* scientific law.

______

______

______

______

______

______

______

Name ______________________________ Date __________

Main Idea — **Details**

Limits of Science

I found this information on page ______.

Complete *the following paragraph by filling in the missing terms from the word bank.*

- bad
- ethics
- explain
- good
- limited
- observed
- scientific methods
- tested

Science is ______________ by what it can ______________.

For a question or problem to be studied through ______________, there must be variables that can be ______________, measured, and ______________. Questions that deal with ______________ or belief systems cannot be answered by science. Ethics is a system of understanding what is ______________ or ______________.

Doing Science Right

I found this information on page ______.

Contrast ethical behavior *in science with* scientific fraud. *Create a table that lists three specific behaviors that are examples of each type of behavior.*

Ethical Behavior	Scientific Fraud

SYNTHESIZE IT

Describe how fraud in scientific research could affect other scientists who research in ethical ways.

____

____

____

Name ______________________________ Date ____________

The Nature of Science Chapter Wrap-Up

Now that you have read the chapter, think about what you have learned and complete the table below. Compare your previous answers with these.

1. Write an **A** if you agree with the statement.
2. Write a **D** if you disagree with the statement.

The Nature of Science	After You Read
• An important part of science is testing, or experimenting.	
• Technology is useful only in the situation for which it was designed.	
• People began studying weather in the 1800s.	
• Science can answer all of the questions that can be asked.	

Review

Use this checklist to help you study.

- ☐ Review the information you included in your Foldable.
- ☐ Study your *Science Notebook* on this chapter.
- ☐ Study the definitions of vocabulary words.
- ☐ Review daily homework assignments.
- ☐ Re-read the chapter and review the charts, graphs, and illustrations.
- ☐ Review the Self Check at the end of each section.
- ☐ Look over the Chapter Review at the end of the chapter.

SUMMARIZE IT **After reading this chapter, identify three things that you have learned about the nature of science.**

____

____

____

____

Name ______________________ Date ______________

Views of Earth

Before You Read

Before you read the chapter, respond to these statements.

1. Write an **A** if you agree with the statement.
2. Write a **D** if you disagree with the statement.

Before You Read	Views of Earth
	• All mountains form in the same way.
	• Lines of longitude run parallel to the equator.
	• All maps of Earth distort the shapes and sizes of landmasses.

Construct the Foldable as directed at the beginning of this chapter.

Science Journal

Assume that you want to build a home and have a satellite photo to guide you. Describe where you would build your new home and why you would build at your chosen location.

Name ______________________ Date __________

Views of Earth

Section 1 Landforms

PS 2.2c: Folded, tilted, faulted, and displaced rock layers suggest past crustal movement. **2.2f:** Plates may collide, move apart, or slide past one another. Most volcanic activity and mountain building occur at the boundaries of these plates, often resulting in earthquakes.

Skim *the headings in Section 1. Write three questions that come to mind from reading these headings.*

1. ______________________
2. ______________________
3. ______________________

Define landform *to show its scientific meaning.*

landform ______________________

____

Write the vocabulary term that matches each definition.

______ large, flat area, often found in the interior regions of continents

______ flat, raised area of land made up of nearly horizontal rocks that have been uplifted by forces within Earth

______ mountain in which rock layers are folded

______ mountain formed when blocks of Earth's crust are pushed up by forces inside Earth

______ mountain made of huge, tilted blocks of rock separated from surrounding rock by faults

______ mountain formed when molten material reaches the surface through a weak area of Earth's crust

Use a dictionary to define **expose.**

expose ______________________

____

Name ______________________ Date __________

Main Idea	Details
Plains *I found this information on page ______.*	**Distinguish** *two reasons that* plains *are useful for agriculture.* 1. ______________________ 2. ______________________
I found this information on page ______.	**Compare and contrast** *coastal plains and interior plains.*

	Coastal Plains	Interior Plains
Location		
Characteristics		

I found this information on page ______.

Summarize *key characteristics of the Great Plains.*

The Great Plains are an example of a(n) ______________. They are located ______________________ ______________. The area is ______________ and covered with ______________. The Great Plains are made of ______________________.

Plateaus

I found this information on page ______.

Compare and contrast *plains and* plateaus. *Complete the Venn diagram with at least three facts.*

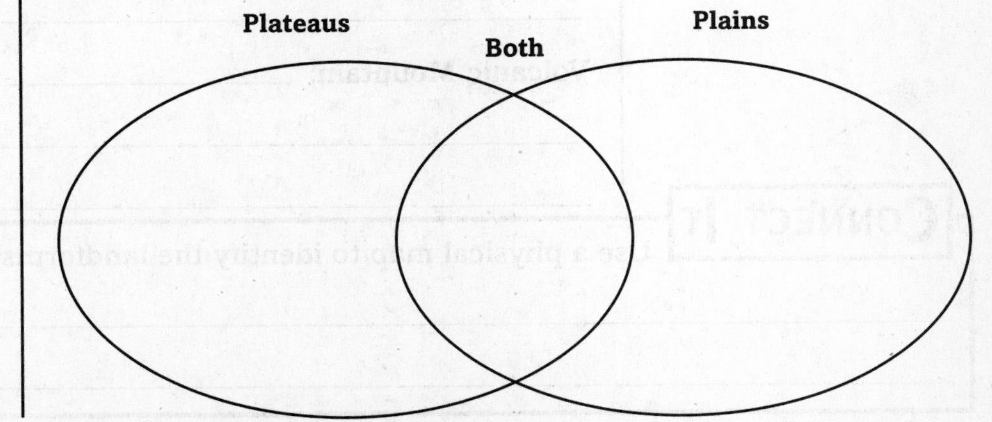

Name ______________________________ Date ____________

Main Idea | **Details**

Mountains

I found this information on page ________.

Model *the four types of* mountains. *Draw a diagram of each type.*

Folded Mountain	**Upwarped Mountain**
Fault-Block Mountain	**Volcanic Mountain**

Summarize *how mountains form. Give an example of each.*

Folded Mountain: ______________________________

____

____

Upwarped Mountain: ______________________________

____

____

Fault-Block Mountain: ______________________________

____

____

Volcanic Mountain: ______________________________

____

____

CONNECT IT Use a physical map to identify the landforms in your area.

____

____

Name ______________________ Date __________

Views of Earth

Section 2 Viewpoints

PS 1.1f: The latitude/longitude coordinate system and our system of time are based on celestial observations.
Also covered: PS 1.1e, 1.1h

Preview *the* What You'll Learn *statements for Section 2. Predict three topics that will be discussed in this section.*

1. ______________________
2. ______________________
3. ______________________

Review Vocabulary **Define** pole *as it is used when describing Earth.*

pole ______________________

New Vocabulary *Define each vocabulary term.*

equator ______________________

latitude ______________________

prime meridian ______________________

longitude ______________________

Academic Vocabulary *Use a dictionary to define* parallel *as an adjective. Then find a sentence in Section 2 that contains the term.*

parallel ______________________

Name ______________________________ Date ______________

Main Idea | **Details**

Latitude and Longitude

I found this information on page ____________.

Model *the system used to measure position on Earth.*

- Draw a view of Earth.
- Label important features on the diagram with the following terms.

equator	prime meridian	90°S latitude
north pole	0° latitude	90°N latitude
south pole		

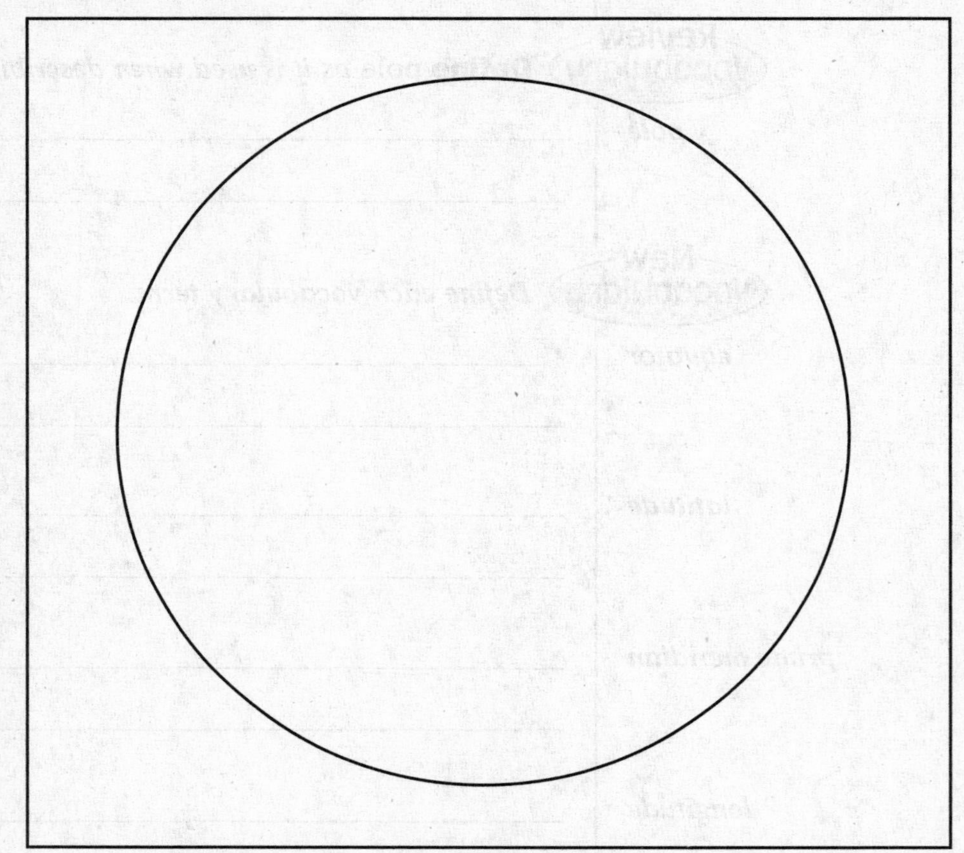

Summarize *how* latitude *and* longitude *are measured.*

Latitude is measured ______________________________

____.

Longitude is measured ______________________________

____.

Degrees of latitude and longitude are divided into ______________

and ______________.

Name ______________________ Date ____________

Section 2 Viewpoints (continued)

Main Idea | **Details**

Time Zones
I found this information on page ________.

Organize *information about time zones. Complete the outline.*

Time Zones

I. Measuring time

A. ______________________

____

B. ______________________

____

II. Characteristics of time zones

A. ______________________

____

B. ______________________

____

C. ______________________

____

Calendar Dates
I found this information on page ________.

Summarize *what a person should do when crossing the International Date Line. Complete the cause-and-effect diagrams.*

Cause		Effect
Travel west across the International Date Line	→	
Travel east across the International Date Line	→	

SYNTHESIZE IT Look at the map of time zones in your book. Infer why the International Date Line does not follow the 180° meridian exactly.

____

____

____

Name ______________________ Date ____________

Views of Earth

Section 3 Maps

AID S1.2b: Propose a model of a natural phenomenon. **Also covered:** AID S3.1b, 6:ICT 2.1, 2.2, 2.3, TPS 1.1f, 2.2g

Scan *the section headings, bold words, and illustrations. Write two facts that you discovered as you scanned the section.*

1. ______________________

2. ______________________

Review Vocabulary

Define globe *to show its scientific meaning.*

globe ______________________

New Vocabulary

Use your book to define each vocabulary term.

conic projection ______________________

topographic map ______________________

contour line ______________________

map scale ______________________

map legend ______________________

Academic Vocabulary

Use a dictionary to define physical. *Use* physical *in a sentence to show its scientific meaning.*

physical ______________________

Name ______________________________ Date __________

Section 3 Maps (continued)

Main Idea / Details

Map Projections

I found this information on page ________.

Define map. *Then complete the statements below about map projections.*

A map is ______________________________.

A map projection is made when ______________________________

______________________________.

All map projections ____________ the shapes and sizes of landmasses to some extent.

I found this information on page ________.

Compare and contrast Mercator, Robinson, *and* conic projections.

	Mercator	Robinson	Conic
How is it made?			
What does it show accurately?			
How is it used?			

Topographic Maps

I found this information on page ________.

Summarize *the purpose of a* topographic map.

____

____

____

____

Main Idea | **Details**

I found this information on page ________.

Organize *information about* contour lines *in the concept web.*

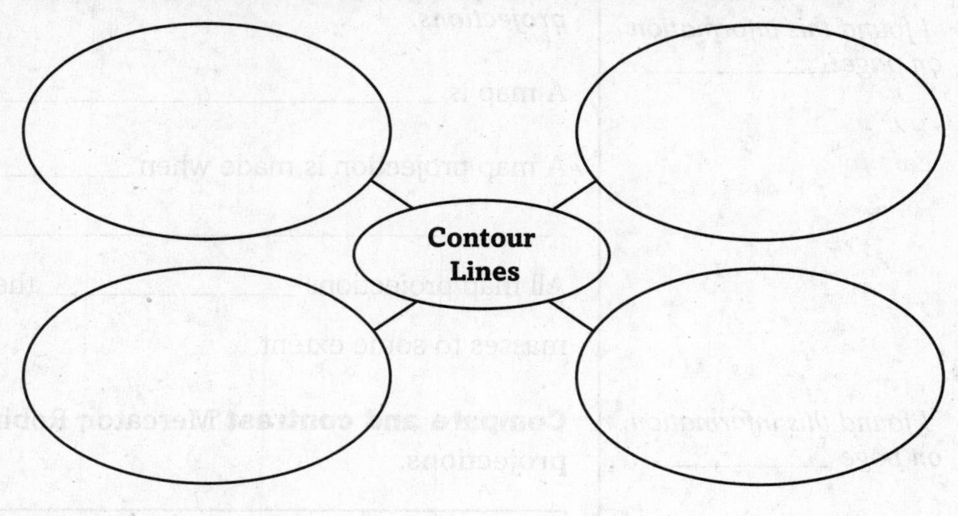

I found this information on page ________.

Summarize *what a* map scale *and* map legend *show.*

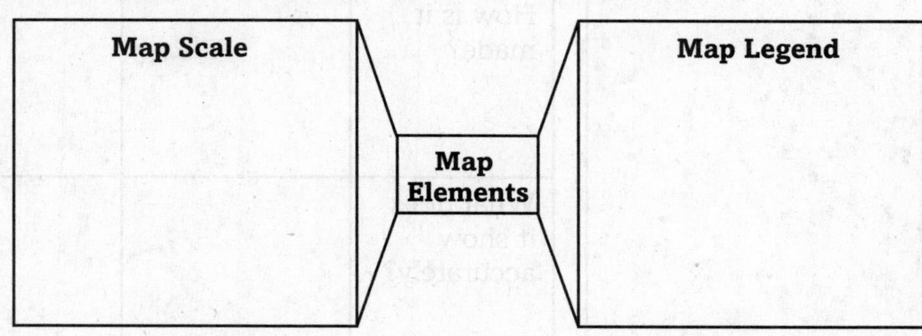

Geologic Maps

I found this information on page ________.

Summarize *what* geologic maps *are and how they are used.*

____

____

____

____

CONNECT IT If you were going to map your classroom, which map scale would be better: 1 cm:1 m or 1 cm: 10 m? Explain your reasoning.

____

____

Name ______________________ Date __________

Tie It Together

Model

Create a two-dimension physical map of your state in the space provided below. Include the major landforms found in your state. Use symbols to indicate these landforms on the map. Be sure to explain the symbols you use in a map legend. Your map should be proportional to the actual size of your state. Include a map scale to help others determine distances.

Name ______________________________ Date ____________

Views of Earth Chapter Wrap-Up

Now that you have read the chapter, think about what you have learned and complete the table below. Compare your previous answers with these.

1. Write an **A** if you agree with the statement.
2. Write a **D** if you disagree with the statement.

Views of Earth	After You Read
• All mountains form in the same way.	
• Lines of longitude run parallel to the equator.	
• All maps of Earth distort the shapes and sizes of landmasses.	

Review

Use this checklist to help you study.

- ☐ Review the information you included in your Foldable.
- ☐ Study your *Science Notebook* on this chapter.
- ☐ Study the definitions of vocabulary words.
- ☐ Review daily homework assignments.
- ☐ Re-read the chapter and review the charts, graphs, and illustrations.
- ☐ Review the Self Check at the end of each section.
- ☐ Look over the Chapter Review at the end of the chapter.

SUMMARIZE IT **Identify three important ideas in this chapter.**

____

____

____

____

Name ______________________ Date ____________

Rocks and Minerals

Before You Read

Before you read the chapter, respond to these statements.

1. Write an **A** if you agree with the statement.
2. Write a **D** if you disagree with the statement.

Before You Read	Rocks and Minerals
	• Minerals are made by people.
	• Most rocks consist of one or more minerals.
	• Rocks are classified in three major groups.
	• Rocks have stopped forming on Earth.
	• Rocks and minerals have many uses in society.

Construct the Foldable as directed at the beginning of this chapter.

Science Journal

Observe a rock or mineral sample. Write three characteristics about it.

Name ______________________________ Date ____________

Rocks and Minerals

Section 1 Minerals—Earth's Jewels

PS 2.1e: Rocks are composed of minerals. Only a few rock-forming minerals make up most of the rocks of Earth. Minerals are identified on the basis of physical properties such as streak, hardness, and reaction to acid. **Also covered:** PS 3.3c

Scan *Section 1 of your book. Then, write three questions that you have about minerals. Try to answer your questions as you read.*

1. ______________________________
2. ______________________________
3. ______________________________

Review Vocabulary

Define physical property *with the help of your book or a dictionary.*

physical property ______________________________

____

____

New Vocabulary

Write the correct vocabulary word from your book next to each definition.

______________ a solid material that has an orderly, repeating pattern of atoms

______________ a mineral that contains enough of a useful substance that it can be mined at a profit

______________ a rare, valuable mineral that can be cut and polished to give it a beautiful appearance

______________ a solid that is usually made up of two or more minerals

Academic Vocabulary

Use a dictionary to find the definition of refine *as it applies to metals. Write the definition below in your own words.*

refine ______________________________

____

Name ____________________ Date __________

Main Idea — **Details**

What is a mineral?

I found this information on page ________.

Complete *the chart below about minerals.*

Minerals
Definition:
Examples:
Ways minerals form: **1.** **2.** **3.**

Properties of Minerals

I found this information on page ________.

Contrast *cleavage and fracture by writing three different characterisitcs of each in the following chart.*

Cleavage	Fracture

I found this information on page ________.

Contrast *the qualities of mineral color and luster.*

Color ____________________

Luster ____________________

Name ______________________ Date __________

Main Idea | **Details**

Common Minerals

I found this information on page ______.

Sequence *four steps that describe how copper ore is turned into useful products. The first step has been completed for you.*

1. Copper ore is mined and crushed.
2. ______________________
3. ______________________
4. ______________________

I found this information on page ______.

List *characteristics of a gem and an ore in the chart below.*

Gem	Ore

CONNECT IT Write the names of six objects in your classroom that are made using minerals. Then explain how minerals are important in your everyday life.

1. __________ 2. __________ 3. __________
4. __________ 5. __________ 6. __________

____

____

____

____

Name ______________________ Date __________

Rocks and Minerals

Section 2 Igneous and Sedimentary Rocks

PS 2.2g: Rocks are classified according to their method of formation. The three classes of rocks are sedimentary, metamorphic, and igneous. Most rocks show characteristics that give clues to their formation conditions. **Also covered:** PS 2.2f, 2.2h

Skim *the headings in Section 2. Then make three predictions about what you will learn.*

1. ______________________

2. ______________________

3. ______________________

Review Vocabulary

Define *the following terms using your book or a dictionary.*

lava ______________________

New Vocabulary

igneous rock ______________________

extrusive ______________________

intrusive ______________________

sedimentary rock ______________________

Academic Vocabulary

process ______________________

Name ______________________ Date __________

Main Idea | **Details**

Igneous Rocks

I found this information on page ______.

Contrast *extrusive and intrusive igneous rocks in the chart.*

Igneous Rocks			
Type	Form from molten rock called	Have cooling rate that is	Have crystal size that is
Extrusive			
Intrusive			

I found this information on page ______.

Organize *a concept map about igneous rocks using these words and phrases.*

- high silica content
- granitic
- low silica content
- dark colored

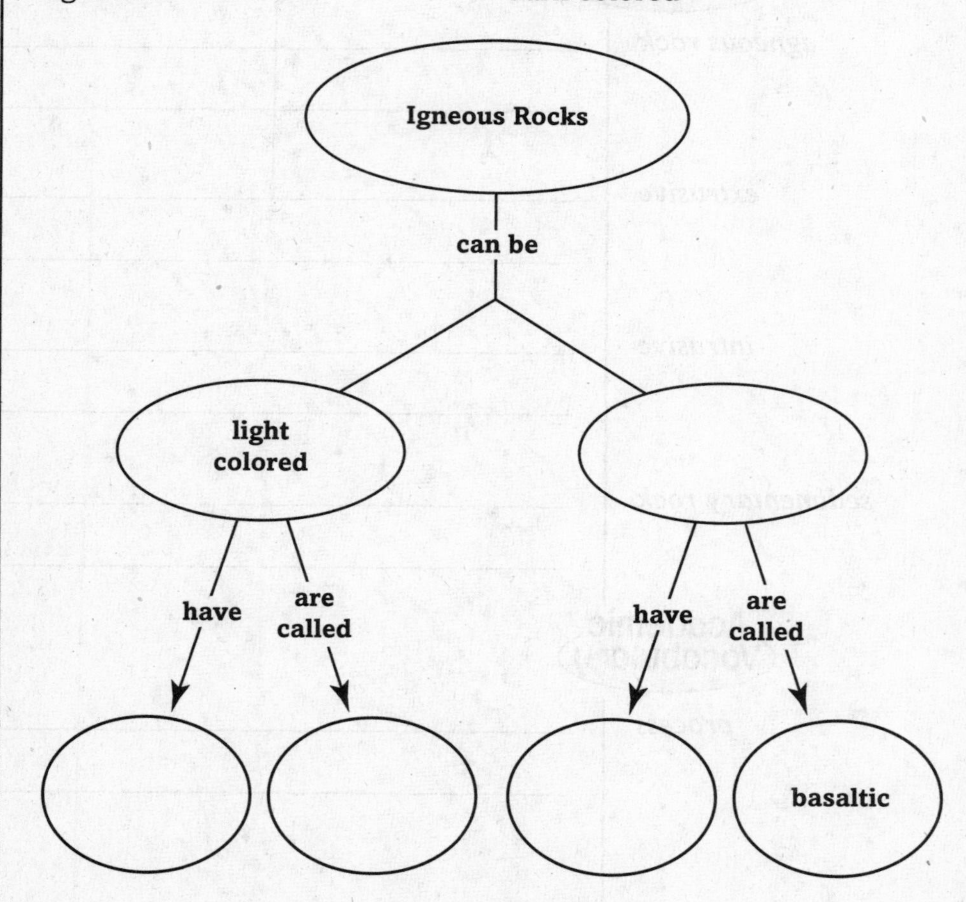

Name ______________________________ Date ______________

Main Idea — **Details**

Sedimentary Rocks

I found this information on page ______.

Classify *sedimentary rocks by some of their characteristics.*

	Detrital	Chemical	Organic
Form from			
How form			
Where form			
Examples			

CONNECT IT **Choose a sedimentary or igneous rock. You might pick basalt, granite, shale, or sandstone. Write a story from the rock's perspective about how the rock formed. When writing your story, you should pretend that you are the rock.**

____

____

____

____

____

____

____

Name ______________________________ Date ____________

Rocks and Minerals

Section 3 Metamorphic Rocks and the Rock Cycle

PS 2.2g: Rocks are classified according to their method of formation. The three classes of rocks are sedimentary, metamorphic, and igneous. Most rocks show characteristics that give clues to their formation conditions. **Also covered:** PS 2.2f, 2.2h

Scan *the headings in Section 3. Write three predictions about what you will learn in this section.*

1. ______________________________
2. ______________________________
3. ______________________________

Review Vocabulary

Define *each vocabulary word. Then, write a sentence reflecting the scientific meaning of each of the words.*

pressure ______________________________

____

New Vocabulary

metamorphic rock ______________________________

____

foliated ______________________________

____

nonfoliated ______________________________

____

rock cycle ______________________________

____

Academic Vocabulary

layer ______________________________

____

Name ______________________ Date __________

Main Idea | **Details**

New Rock from Old

I found this information on page ______.

Summarize *the conditions under which rocks experience metamorphism as you complete the chart below.*

Conditions of Metamorphic Rock Formation	
temperature	
pressure	
time	

I found this information on page ______.

Draw *a metamorphic rock with a foliated texture and a metamorphic rock with a nonfoliated texture below. Show and label two characteristics of each type of rock in the top boxes, and list an example of each type in the bottom boxes.*

Foliated texture	Nonfoliated texture
Examples:	Examples:

Name ______________________ Date __________

Main Idea | **Details**

Rock Cycle

I found this information on page ______.

Create *a diagram of the rock cycle below.*

- Label each type of rock in your diagram.
- Label the processes in your diagram. Use the words *melting, cooling, weathering and erosion, compaction and cementation,* and *heat and pressure.*

Identify *two other cycles that occur in nature.*

1. ______________________
2. ______________________

CONNECT IT While on a leisurely hike, a geologist from the nearby university noticed that the gravel in a sedimentary rock consists of pieces of both igneous and metamorphic rock. As the geologist, write a brief report explaining how this is possible.

____

____

____

Name ______________________ Date ____________

Tie It Together

Design

Some artists specialize in making art from rock and mineral pieces. The different colors, textures, and other properties of the rocks and minerals can produce spectacular displays. In the space below, design your own rock and mineral art. It might be mounted on a wall, make up the courtyard of a building, or be a large monument. You may use any rock or mineral shown in your book in your art.

Name ______________________________ Date ____________

Rocks and Minerals Chapter Wrap-Up

Now that you have read the chapter, think about what you have learned and complete the table below. Compare your previous answers with these.

1. Write an **A** if you agree with the statement.
2. Write a **D** if you disagree with the statement.

Rocks and Minerals	After You Read
• Minerals are made by people.	
• Most rocks consist of one or more minerals.	
• Rocks are classified in three major groups.	
• Rocks have stopped forming on Earth.	
• Rocks and minerals have many uses in society.	

Review

Use this checklist to help you study.

- ☐ Review the information you included in your Foldable.
- ☐ Study your *Science Notebook* on this chapter.
- ☐ Study the definitions of vocabulary words.
- ☐ Review daily homework assignments.
- ☐ Re-read the chapter and review the charts, graphs, and illustrations.
- ☐ Review the Self Check at the end of each section.
- ☐ Look over the Chapter Review at the end of the chapter.

SUMMARIZE IT **After reading this chapter, identify three things that you have learned about rocks and minerals.**

____

____

____

____

Name ______________________________ Date ______________

Weathering and Erosion

Before You Read

Before you read the chapter, respond to these statements.

1. Write an **A** if you agree with the statement.
2. Write a **D** if you disagree with the statement.

Before You Read	Weathering and Erosion
	• Weathering is the conditions of the atmosphere at a given time.
	• Soil forms from pieces of broken rock and other kinds of matter.
	• Erosion moves rock and soil from one place to another.
	• Water can cause erosion, but ice cannot.

Construct the Foldable as directed at the beginning of this chapter.

Science Journal

Describe a place—a home, a park, a river, or a mountain. What might that place look like in a year, a hundred years, even 5,000 years?

Name ______________________ Date ______________

Weathering and Erosion

Section 1 Weathering and Soil Formation

PS 2.1g: The dynamic processes that wear away Earth's surface include weathering and erosion. **2.1h:** The process of weathering breaks down rocks to form sediment. Soil consists of sediment, organic material, water, and air.

Skim *through Section 1 of your book. Read the headings and look at the illustrations. Write three questions that come to mind.*

1. ______________________
2. ______________________
3. ______________________

Review Vocabulary

Define *the key terms using your book or a dictionary.*

acid rain ______________________

New Vocabulary

weathering ______________________

mechanical weathering ______________________

chemical weathering ______________________

soil ______________________

topography ______________________

Academic Vocabulary

Define chemical *as an adjective. Use a dictionary to help you.*

chemical ______________________

Main Idea | **Details**

Weathering

I found this information on page ____________.

Organize *information by listing three things that cause rocks to weather.*

Causes of Weathering	
1.	
2.	
3.	

Mechanical Weathering

I found this information on page ____________.

Identify *major causes of mechanical weathering. Complete the concept map below.*

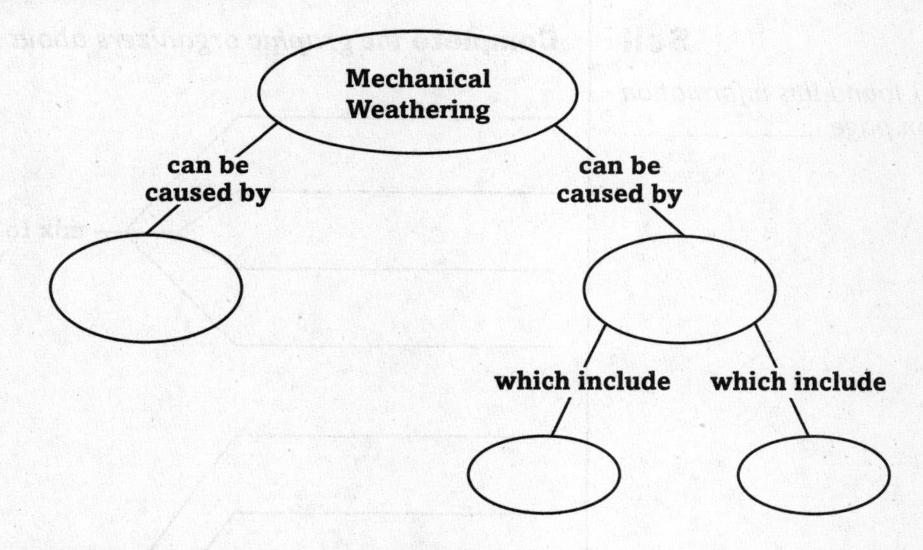

I found this information on page ____________.

Create *three drawings to show the process of ice wedging.*

Water seeps into cracks.	Water freezes and expands, making cracks wider.	Ice melts and the process repeats.

Name ______________________________ Date ____________

Main Idea | **Details**

Chemical Weathering

I found this information on page ________.

Organize *the information from your book in the outline below.*

Chemical weathering

A. Definition: ______________________________

____

B. Causes:

1. ______________________________

2. ______________________________

3. ______________________________

Soil

I found this information on page ________.

Complete *the graphic organizers about soil and soil formation.*

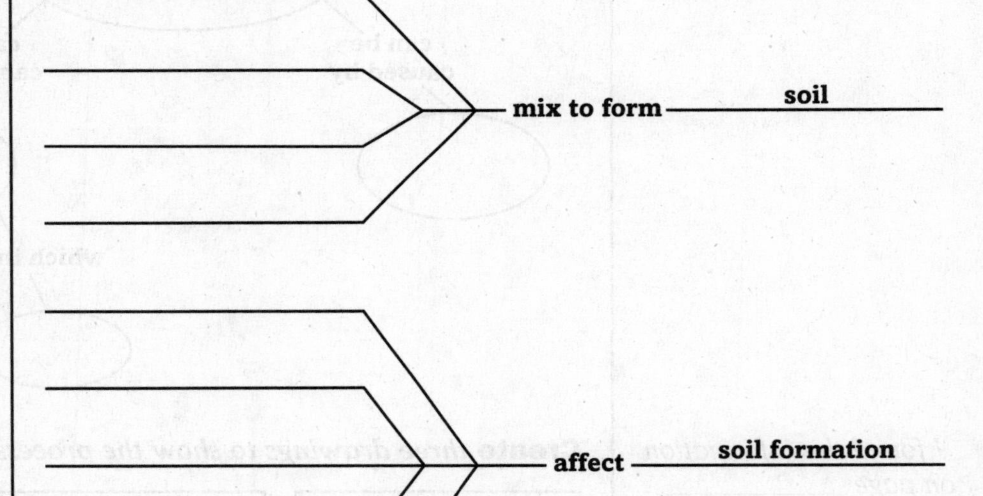

CONNECT IT The temperature on some mountains is below freezing all year. Predict what soil on these mountains is like.

____

____

____

Name ______________________ Date __________

Weathering and Erosion

Section 2 Erosion of Earth's Surface

PS 2.1i: Erosion is the transport of sediment. Gravity is the driving force behind erosion. Gravity can act directly or through agents such as moving water, wind, and glaciers. **Also covered:** PS 2.1g

Scan *Use the checklist below to preview Section 2 of your book. Then write three facts that you discovered about how erosion affects Earth's surface.*

☐ Read all headings.

☐ Read all boldface words.

☐ Look at all of the pictures.

☐ Think about what you already know about features of Earth's surface.

1. ______________________

2. ______________________

3. ______________________

Review Vocabulary

Write the correct vocabulary word next to each definition.

______________ the dropping of sediment that occurs when an agent of erosion can no longer carry its load

New Vocabulary

______________ the movement of rock or soil by gravity, ice, wind, or water

______________ erosion that occurs when gravity alone causes rock or sediment to move down a slope

______________ the process in which sediment moves slowly downhill

______________ the movement of rock or sediment downhill along a curved surface

______________ the erosion of the land by wind

______________ erosion that occurs when wind blows sediment into rocks, makes pits in the rocks, and produces a smooth, polished surface

______________ water that flows over the ground

Academic Vocabulary

Define occur *using a dictionary.*

occur ______________________

Name ______________________ Date __________

Main Idea **Details**

Agents of Erosion

I found this information on page ______.

Organize *information from your book by filling in the concept map with the four agents, or causes, of erosion.*

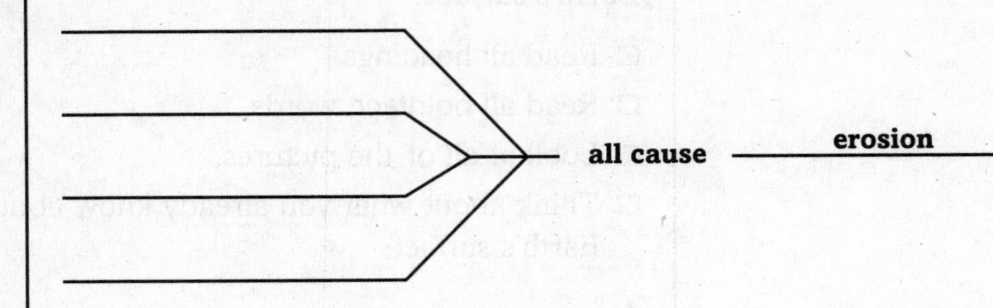

Gravity

I found this information on page ______.

Compare and contrast *the four types of mass movements. Write ways they are all the same and some ways they are different.*

Mass Movements	
Similarities	**Differences**

Ice

I found this information on page ______.

Sequence *four steps explaining how glaciers form and change Earth's surface.*

Glaciers Form and Change Earth's Surface	
1.	
2.	
3.	
4.	

Name ______________________________ Date ____________

Main Idea | **Details**

Wind

I found this information on page ____________.

Model *how a sand dune moves by making a diagram in the box. Label the following features:*

- sand blows up this side
- sand falls down this side
- dune movement (arrow)
- wind (arrow)

Water

I found this information on page ____________.

Complete *the concept map by listing several ways that water can flow over Earth's surface.*

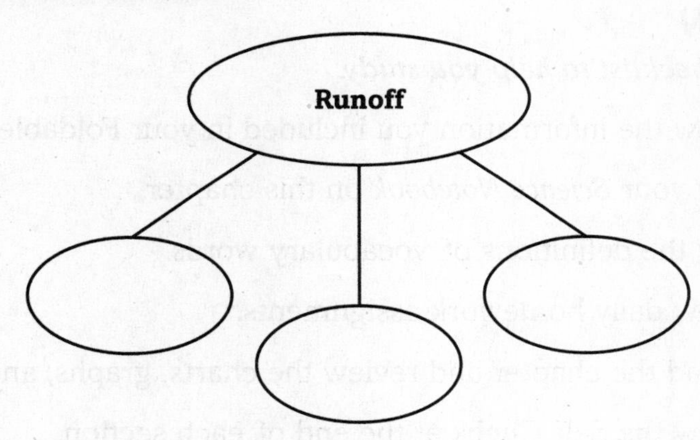

Effects of Erosion

I found this information on page ____________.

Analyze *the effects of erosion. List three examples of landforms caused by erosion and three examples caused by deposition.*

Effects of Erosion	
Where Sediment is Removed (erosion)	Where Sediment Accumulates (deposition)

Name ______________________________ Date ____________

Weathering and Erosion

Chapter Wrap-Up

Now that you have read the chapter, think about what you have learned and complete the table below. Compare your previous answers with these.

1. Write an **A** if you agree with the statement.
2. Write a **D** if you disagree with the statement.

Weathering and Erosion	After You Read
• Weathering is the conditions of the atmosphere at a given time.	
• Soil forms from pieces of broken rock and other kinds of matter.	
• Erosion moves rock and soil from one one place to another.	
• Water can cause erosion, but ice cannot.	

Review

Use this checklist to help you study.

- ☐ Review the information you included in your Foldable.
- ☐ Study your *Science Notebook* on this chapter.
- ☐ Study the definitions of vocabulary words.
- ☐ Review daily homework assignments.
- ☐ Re-read the chapter and review the charts, graphs, and illustrations.
- ☐ Review the Self Check at the end of each section.
- ☐ Look over the Chapter Review at the end of the chapter.

SUMMARIZE IT **After reading this chapter, identify three things that you have learned about weathering and erosion.**

____

____

____

____

Name ______________________________ Date ____________

Clues to Earth's Past

Before You Read

Before you read the chapter, respond to these statements.

1. Write an **A** if you agree with the statement.
2. Write a **D** if you disagree with the statement.

Before You Read	Clues to Earth's Past
	• The footprint of a dinosaur is considered a fossil.
	• Scientists use fossils to learn what an environment was like long ago.
	• The oldest rock layer is always the one found on top.
	• Scientists can determine the age of some rocks.

Construct the Foldable as directed at the beginning of this chapter.

Science Journal

List three fossils that you would expect to find a million years from now in the place you live today.

____

____

____

____

____

____

Name ______________________ Date ____________

Clues to Earth's Past

Section 1 Fossils

LE 3.2b: Extinction of a species occurs when the environment changes and the adaptive characteristics of a species are insufficient to permit its survival. **PS 2.1f:** Fossils are usually found in sedimentary rocks. Fossils can be used to study past climates and environments. **Also covered:** LE 3.2c

Skim *Section 1 of your book. Read the headings and examine the illustrations. Write three questions that come to mind.*

1. ______________________
2. ______________________
3. ______________________

Review Vocabulary **Define** paleontologist *to show its scientific meaning.*

paleontologist ______________________

New Vocabulary *Define the following terms to show their scientific meaning.*

permineralized remains ______________________

carbon film ______________________

cast ______________________

index fossils ______________________

Academic Vocabulary *Define* emerge *to show its scientific meaning.*

emerge ______________________

Name ______________________ Date __________

Main Idea | **Details**

Formation of Fossils

I found this information on page ______.

Complete *the chart to describe the two conditions that improve the chances of* fossil *formation. Give an example of each.*

Condition	Example

Types of Preservation

I found this information on page ______.

Create *a concept web to summarize the types of preservation.*

I found this information on page ______.

Sequence *the steps involved in the making of the* cast *of a shell.*

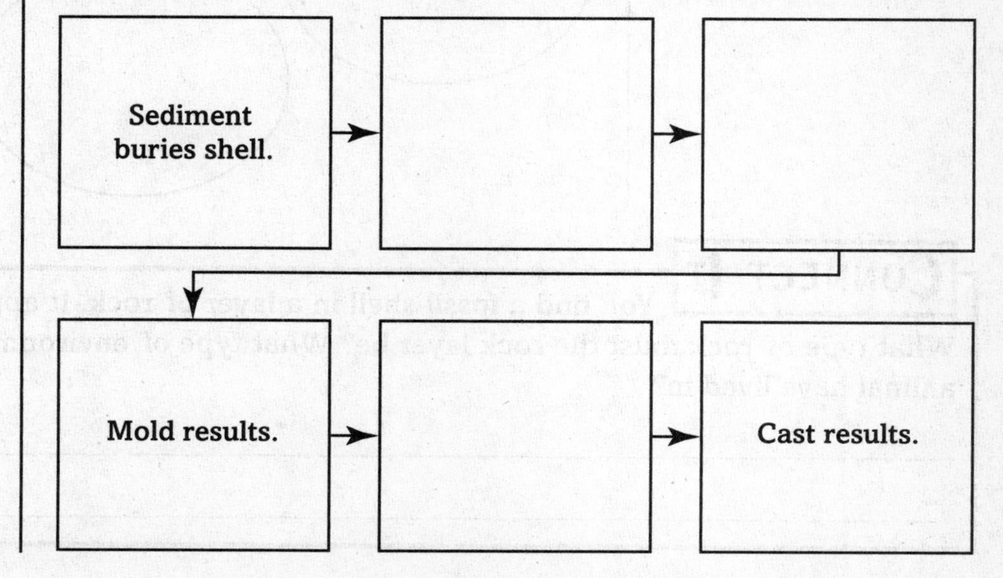

Name ______________________ Date __________

Main Idea	Details
Index Fossils *I found this information on page* ______.	**Summarize** *the three characteristics of* index fossils. **1.** ______ **2.** ______ **3.** ______ **Analyze** *why index fossils are more useful to paleontologists than many other fossils.* ______ ______ ______ ______
Fossils and Ancient Environments *I found this information on page* ______.	**Organize** *the kinds of information about ancient environments that scientists can learn from fossils. Complete the graphic organizer.*

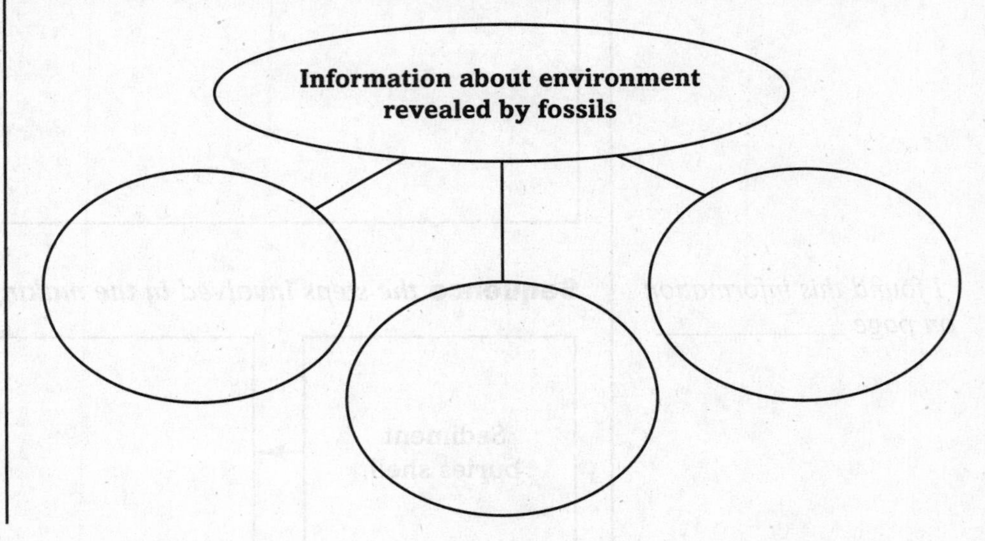

CONNECT IT You find a fossil shell in a layer of rock. It appears to be a clam. What type of rock must the rock layer be? What type of environment would the animal have lived in?

______

______

Name ______________________________ Date ____________

Clues to Earth's Past

Section 2 Relative Ages of Rocks

LE 3.2c: Many thousands of layers of sedimentary rock provide evidence for the long history of Earth and for the long history of changing lifeforms whose remains are found in the rocks. Recently deposited rock layers are more likely to contain fossils resembling existing species. **Also covered:** PS 2.2c

Scan *the list below to preview Section 2 of your book.*

- Read all section headings.
- Read all bold words.
- Look at all of the pictures.
- Think about what you already know about rock.

Write three facts you discovered about the relative ages of rocks as you scanned the section.

1. ______________________________

2. ______________________________

3. ______________________________

Define sedimentary rock *to show its scientific meaning.*

sedimentary rock ______________________________

____

Read each definition below. Write the correct vocabulary term in the blank to the left.

______________ states that in undisturbed rock layers, the oldest rocks are on the bottom and the rocks are progressively younger toward the top

______________ age of something compared with the ages of other things

______________ gap in a sequence of rock layers that is due to erosion or periods without any deposition

Academic Vocabulary

Define* sequence *to show its scientific meaning.

sequence ______________________________

____

Name ______________________________ Date ____________

Main Idea | Details

Superposition

I found this information on page ____________.

Model *the* principle of superposition *by sketching a cross-section of layers of undisturbed sedimentary rock. Number the layers, starting with 1 for the oldest layer.*

Relative Ages

I found this information on page ____________.

Describe *how the* relative age *of a rock layer is different from the actual age of the rock layer.*

____

____

____

____

____

____

I found this information on page ____________.

Model *how a folded rock formation containing limestone, coal, and sandstone would form. Draw and label the layers as they would form originally. Then draw what they would look like after being folded.*

Name ______________________ Date __________

Main Idea | **Details**

Unconformities

I found this information on page ________.

Compare and contrast angular unconformity, disconformity, *and* nonconformity *in rocks by sequencing the steps in their formation.*

Unconformities	
Type	**How It Forms**
Angular unconformity	**1.** **2.** **3.**
Disconformity	**1.** **2.** **3.**
Nonconformity	**1.** **2.** **3.**

Matching Up Rock Layers

I found this information on page ________.

Identify *the two ways to match up, or correlate, exposed rock layers from two different places. Complete the graphic organizer.*

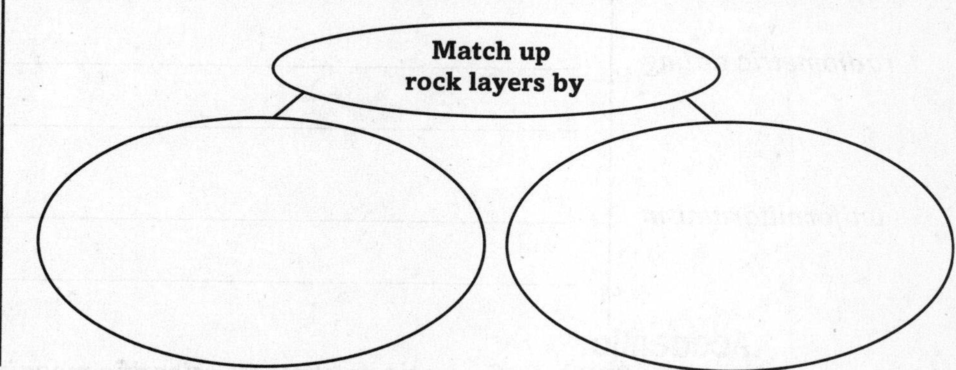

SYNTHESIZE IT As you pass through a highway cut, you notice distinct layers of rock. Can you be sure that the top layer is the youngest one? Explain.

____

____

Name ______________________ Date __________

Clues to Earth's Past

Section 3 Absolute Ages of Rocks

LE 3.2c: Many thousands of layers of sedimentary rock provide evidence for the long history of Earth and for the long history of changing lifeforms whose remains are found in the rocks. Recently deposited rock layers are more likely to contain fossils resembling existing species. **Also covered:** PS 3.3a

Predict *three things that might be discussed in Section 3 as you read the headings.*

1. ______________________

2. ______________________

3. ______________________

Review Vocabulary

Define isotopes *to show its scientific meaning.*

isotopes ______________________

New Vocabulary

Define these key terms to show their scientific meaning.

radioactive decay ______________________

radiometric dating ______________________

uniformitarianism ______________________

Academic Vocabulary

Define ratio *to show its scientific meaning.*

ratio ______________________

Main Idea **Details**

Absolute Ages and **Radioactive Decay**

I found this information on page ____________.

Organize *information about* radioactive decay *as a tool to find a rock's absolute age. Complete the Venn diagram below with at least six points of information.*

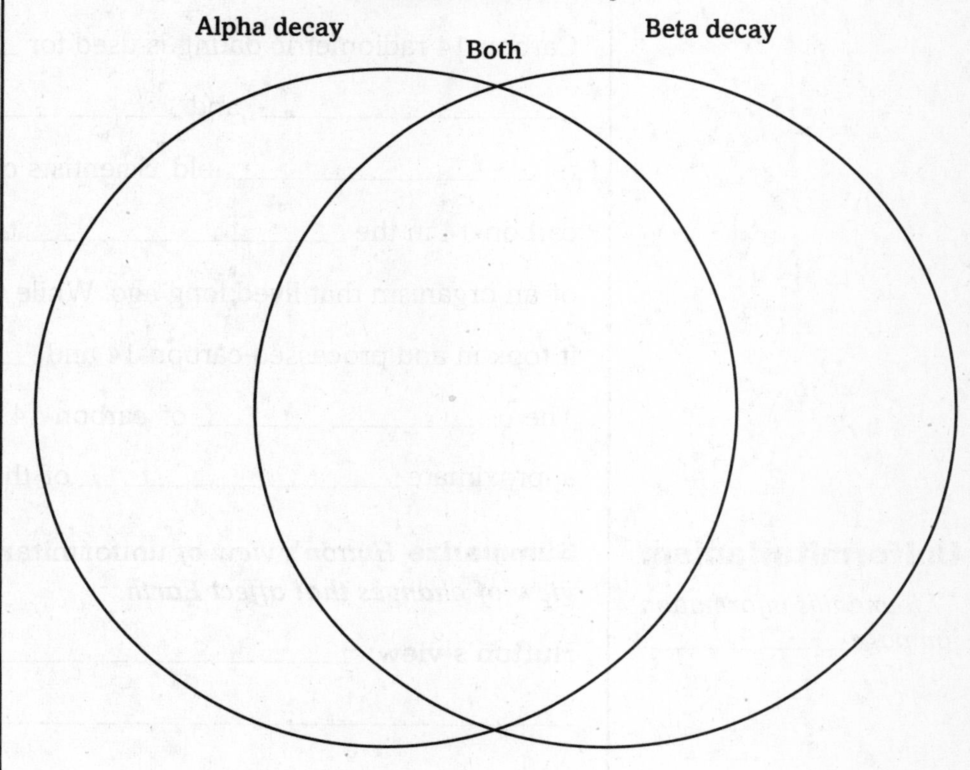

I found this information on page ____________.

Create *a bar chart to show four* half-lives. *Then draw a curve connecting the tops of the bars. Label each axis.*

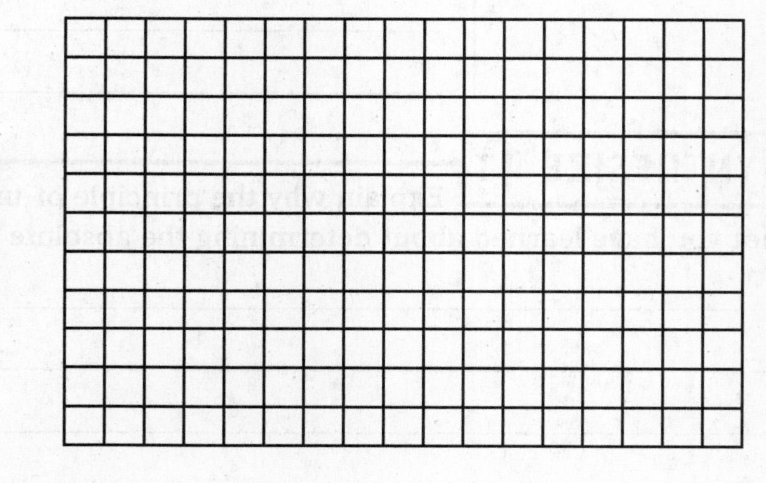

Name ______________________ Date ____________

Main Idea | **Details**

Radiometric Ages

I found this information on page ________.

Analyze *carbon-14 dating by completing the statements.*

The half-life of carbon-14 is ____________________.

When carbon-14 decays, it becomes ____________________.

Carbon-14 radiometric dating is used for ____________________, ____________________, and ____________________ samples up to ____________________ old. Scientists compare amounts of carbon-14 in the ____________________ to the amount in a fossil of an organism that lived long ago. While the organism was alive, it took in and processed carbon-14 and ____________________. The ____________________ of carbon-14 to carbon-12 tells the approximate ____________________ of the fossil.

Uniformitarianism

I found this information on page ________.

Summarize *Hutton's view of* uniformitarianism *and the modern view of changes that affect Earth.*

Hutton's view: ____________________

____

____

Modern view: ____________________

____

____

SYNTHESIZE IT Explain why the principle of uniformitarianism is critical to what you have learned about determining the absolute age of rocks.

____

____

____

____

Name ______________________________ Date ____________

Tie It Together

A paleontologist found the following composition of rock layers at a site. The paleontologist concludes that no folding or other disruption has happened to the layers. What can you conclude about the area's history? Write a summary of your conclusions.

Top layer: coal layer made up of altered plant material

Middle layer: mix of sandstone and shale, with some tracks made by dinosaurs

Bottom layer: limestone with fossils of clams, snails, and sea lilies

Name ________________________________ Date ____________

Clues to Earth's Past Chapter Wrap-Up

Now that you have read the chapter, think about what you have learned and complete the table below. Compare your previous answers with these.

1. Write an **A** if you agree with the statement.
2. Write a **D** if you disagree with the statement.

Clues to Earth's Past	After You Read
• The footprint of a dinosaur is considered a fossil.	
• Scientists use fossils to learn what an environment was like long ago.	
• The oldest rock layer is always the one found on top.	
• Scientists can determine the age of some rocks.	

Review

Use this checklist to help you study.

- ☐ Review the information you included in your Foldable.
- ☐ Study your *Science Notebook* on this chapter.
- ☐ Study the definitions of vocabulary words.
- ☐ Review daily homework assignments.
- ☐ Re-read the chapter and review the charts, graphs, and illustrations.
- ☐ Review the Self Check at the end of each section.
- ☐ Look over the Chapter Review at the end of the chapter.

SUMMARIZE IT **Identify three facts about fossils and rock layers that you found interesting.**

____

____

____

____

Name ______________________________ Date ______________

Plate Tectonics

Before You Read

Before you read the chapter, respond to these statements.

1. Write an **A** if you agree with the statement.
2. Write a **D** if you disagree with the statement.

Before You Read	Plate Tectonics
	• Fossil evidence provides support for the idea that continents have moved over time.
	• New seafloor is continuously forming while old seafloor is being destroyed.
	• Earth's crust is broken into sections called plates.
	• Rock flows deep inside Earth.

Construct the Foldable as directed at the beginning of this chapter.

Science Journal

Pretend you're a journalist with an audience that assumes the continents have never moved. Write about the kinds of evidence you'll need to convince people otherwise.

Name ______________________ Date __________

Plate Tectonics

Section 1 Continental Drift

A **PS 2.2d:** Continents fitting together like puzzle parts and fossil correlations provided initial evidence that continents were once together. **Also covered:** PS 2.2c

Skim *through Section 1 of your book. Write three questions that come to mind from reading the headings and examining the illustrations.*

1. ______________________

2. ______________________

3. ______________________

Review Vocabulary **Define** continent *to show its scientific meaning.*

continent ______________________

New Vocabulary *Use your book to define the following terms. Then write an original sentence using each term.*

continental drift ______________________

Pangaea ______________________

Academic Vocabulary *Use a dictionary to define* controversy.

controversy ______________________

Name ______________________ Date __________

Main Idea

Details

Evidence for Continental Drift

I found this information on page ______.

Summarize Alfred Wegener's hypothesis *about Earth's continents.*

____

____

____

____

____

I found this information on page ______.

Create *a graphic organizer to identify the three types of clues that are evidence for* continental drift.

I found this information on page ______.

Analyze *the clue in the left column below. Then describe how Alfred Wegener would have explained it in the right column.*

Clue	Wegener's Response
Fossils of Mesosaurus found in South America and Africa	
Fossil plant found in five continents, including Antarctica	
Fossils of warm weather plants found on Arctic island	
Glacial deposits found in Africa, India, and Australia	

Name ____________________ Date ____________

Main Idea / Details

I found this information on page ______.

Model *what the continents may have looked like 250 million years ago.*

How could continents drift?

I found this information on page ______.

Summarize *Wegener's explanations of how and why continental drift occurs.*

Wegener's explanation for continental drift

How: ____________________

Why: ____________________

EVALUATE IT

Do you think it was reasonable for scientists initially to reject the hypothesis of continental drift? Explain your response.

____

Name ______________________________ Date ______________

Plate Tectonics

Section 2 Seafloor Spreading

PS 2.2a: The interior of Earth is hot. Heat flow and movement of material within Earth cause sections of Earth's crust to move. This may result in earthquakes, volcanic eruption, and the creation of mountains and ocean basins.

Predict *three things that might be discussed in Section 2 after reading its headings.*

1. ______________________________

2. ______________________________

3. ______________________________

Review Vocabulary

Define seafloor. *Then use the word in a sentence.*

seafloor ______________________________

New Vocabulary

Use your book to define seafloor spreading. *Then use the term in a sentence.*

seafloor spreading ______________________________

Academic Vocabulary

Use a dictionary to define interval. *Then use the word in a sentence about magnetic clues to seafloor spreading.*

interval ______________________________

Name ______________________________ Date ______________

Main Idea	Details
Mapping the Ocean Floor *I found this information on page ______.*	**Summarize** *how sound waves are used to map the seafloor.* ______________________________ ______________________________ ______________________________ ______________________________
I found this information on page ______.	**Model** *the process of* seafloor spreading *by drawing a cross section of a mid-ocean ridge and the magma below it. Use arrows to indicate the directions of motion.*

Sequence *steps describing seafloor spreading.*

Hot, less dense material below Earth's crust rises toward the surface at a mid-ocean ridge.

↓

The less dense material flows ______________________________.

↓

As the seafloor spreads apart, magma is ______________________________.

Name ______________________________ Date ______________

Main Idea | **Details**

Evidence for Spreading

I found this information on page ______.

Label *the diagram below to identify evidence for seafloor spreading. Add arrows to show the direction of spreading, and indicate where older rock and newer rock occur.*

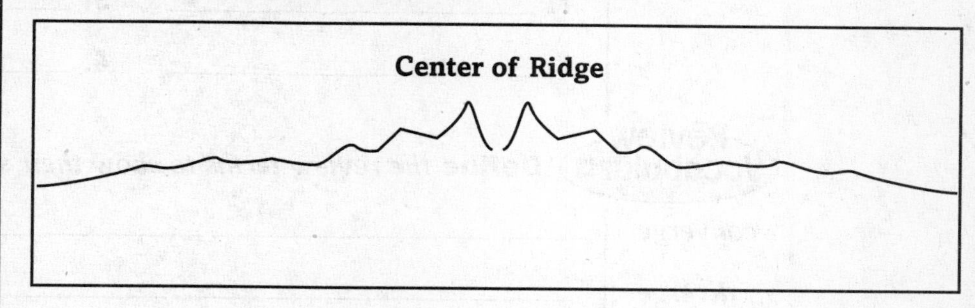

I found this information on page ______.

Model *the polarity of Earth's magnetic field today.*

- Draw a sphere to represent Earth.
- Label the north pole and south pole.
- Draw arrows indicating the direction in which magnetic lines of force enter and leave Earth.

Summarize *how reversals in the direction of Earth's magnetic field have provided evidence of seafloor spreading.*

At times, the ______________________ that pass through Earth have ______________________. ______________ of Earth's magnetic field are recorded in ______________ that forms along ______________________. Scientists can detect ______________________ that are ______________ to mid-ocean ridges. This occurs on ______________________.

Name ______________________________ Date ____________

Plate Tectonics

Section 3 Theory of Plate Tectonics

PS 2.2e: The Theory of Plate Tectonics explains how the "solid" lithosphere consists of a series of plates that "float" on the partially molten section of the mantle. Convection cells within the mantle may be the driving force for the movement of the plates. **Also covered:** PS 2.1c, 2.2b, 2.2c, 2.2f

Scan *the headings and illustrations in Section 3. List four features caused by plate tectonics.*

1. ____________ 3. ____________

2. ____________ 4. ____________

Review Vocabulary

Define *the review terms to show their scientific meanings.*

converge ____________

diverge ____________

transform ____________

New Vocabulary

Use your book to define the following terms.

plate ____________

plate tectonics ____________

lithosphere ____________

asthenosphere ____________

convection current ____________

Academic Vocabulary

Use a dictionary to define rigid.

rigid ____________

Name ______________________________ Date ______________

Main Idea | **Details**

Plate Tectonics

I found this information on page ______.

Complete *the following outline on the theory of* plate tectonics.

I. A new theory
   A. In the 1960s, a new theory called ______________ was developed.
   B. Earth's ______________ and part of the ______________ are broken into sections called ______________, that move slowly.

II. Details about the theory
   A. The layer of Earth that is broken into sections is called the ______________.
   B. The ______________ is the plasticlike layer below the ______________.
   C. The rigid plates move over the ______________.

Plate Boundaries

I found this information on page ______.

Compare and contrast *the different* plate *boundaries by defining them side by side. Draw the plates of the world. Identify plate motion by using arrows.*

Divergent	Convergent	Transform

Main Idea | **Details**

Causes of Plate Tectonics

I found this information on page ________.

Label *the* convection currents *depicted below with heating, rising, cooling, and sinking.*

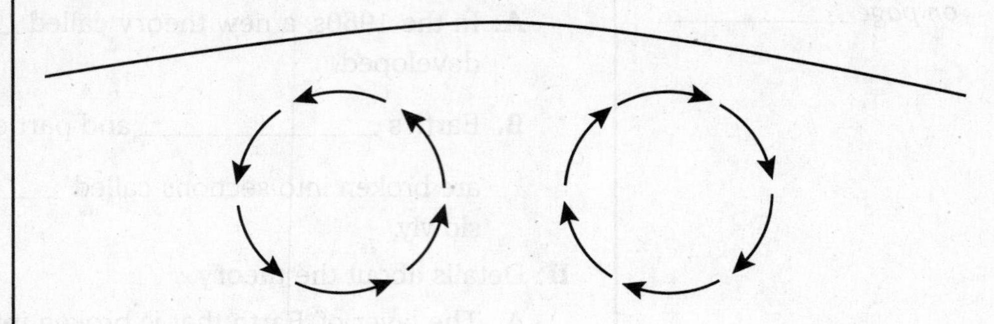

Features Caused by Plate Tectonics

I found this information on page ________.

Organize *information to describe features caused by plate tectonics. Fill in the chart below.*

Feature	Description
Rift valley	
Folded and faulted mountains	
Strike-slip faults	

Testing for Plate Tectonics

I found this information on page ________.

Summarize *how the Satellite Laser Ranging System measures plate movement.*

____

____

____

____

____

Name ______________________ Date ____________

Tie It Together

Synthesize It

Your book has a picture showing how continents may have drifted. It shows their positions 250 million years ago, 125 million years ago, and at the present. Work with a partner to trace the paths that the continents have taken. Then extend their paths forward in time to project where they may be 125 million years from now. Draw a map in the space below, showing your prediction.

Name ______________________ Date ____________

Plate Tectonics Chapter Wrap-Up

Now that you have read the chapter, think about what you have learned and complete the table below. Compare your previous answers with these.

1. Write an **A** if you agree with the statement.
2. Write a **D** if you disagree with the statement.

Plate Tectonics	After You Read
• Fossil evidence provides support for the idea that continents have moved over time.	
• New seafloor is continuously forming while old seafloor is being destroyed.	
• Earth's crust is broken into sections called plates.	
• Rock flows deep inside Earth.	

Review

Use this checklist to help you study.

- ☐ Review the information you included in your Foldable.
- ☐ Study your *Science Notebook* on this chapter.
- ☐ Study the definitions of vocabulary words.
- ☐ Review daily homework assignments.
- ☐ Re-read the chapter and review the charts, graphs, and illustrations.
- ☐ Review the Self Check at the end of each section.
- ☐ Look over the Chapter Review at the end of the chapter.

SUMMARIZE IT **After reading this chapter, identify three things that you have learned about plate tectonics.**

____

____

____

____

Name ______________________________ Date ____________

Earthquakes and Volcanoes

Before You Read

Preview the chapter title, the section titles, and the section headings. Complete the first two columns of the chart by listing at least two ideas for each section in each column.

K What I know	W What I want to learn

Construct the Foldable as directed at the beginning of this chapter.

Science Journal

Are earthquakes and volcanoes completely unrelated, or could there be a possible connection? Propose several ideas that might explain what causes these events.

Name ______________________________ Date ____________

Earthquakes and Volcanoes

Section 1 Earthquakes

PS 2.2a: The interior of Earth is hot. Heat flow and movement of material within Earth cause sections of Earth's crust to move. This may result in earthquakes, volcanic eruption, and the creation of mountains and ocean basins. **2.2c:** Folded, tilted, faulted, and displaced rock layers suggest past crustal movement. **Also covered:** PS 2.2b, 2.2f

Scan *the headings in Section 1 and write three questions you have about earthquakes.*

1. ______________________________
2. ______________________________
3. ______________________________

Review Vocabulary

energy

New Vocabulary

earthquake

fault

seismic wave

focus

epicenter

seismograph

magnitude

tsunami

seismic safe

Academic Vocabulary

collapse

Write six original sentences with at least two vocabulary terms in each. Include the review, new, and academic vocabulary items. Underline the vocabulary terms that you use. Words may be used more than once. Use all of the words.

____

Main Idea | **Details**

What causes earthquakes?

I found this information on page ______.

Model *the direction of motion in the three types of* faults *below. Use arrows to indicate direction of force and direction of movement. Label the arrows.*

Normal Fault

Reverse Fault

Strike-slip Fault

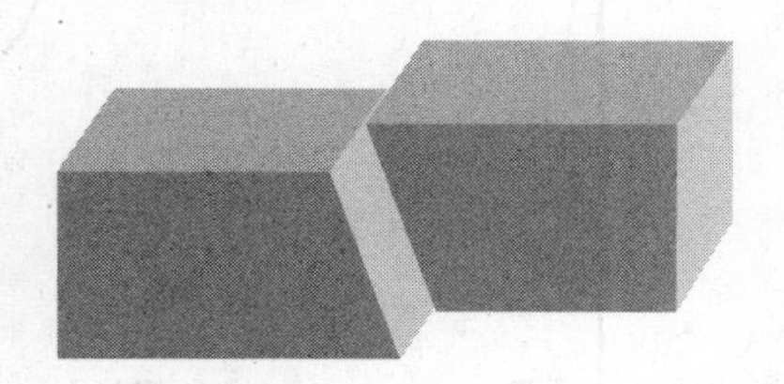

Making Waves

I found this information on page ______.

Compare *primary, secondary, and surface* seismic waves *by completing the chart below. Put an* **X** *in the column of the type of wave that causes the most damage.*

Seismic Waves			
	Primary	Secondary	Surface
Most damage			
Relative speed			
Motion			
Where they travel			

Main Idea | **Details**

Learning from Earthquakes

I found this information on page ________.

Model *how an earthquake's* epicenter *is located. The stars in the diagram indicate* seismograph *stations. The circles show their distance from the epicenter. Mark the epicenter with an* **X**, *and use arrows to show the directions in which* seismic waves *travel.*

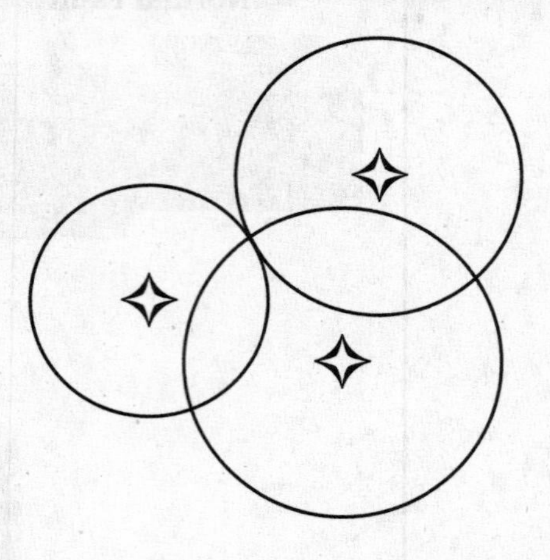

How strong are earthquakes?

I found this information on page ________.

Compare *the Richter scale and the Mercalli scale in the chart.*

Comparing Earthquake Scales	
Richter	Mercalli

Earthquake Safety

I found this information on page ________.

Organize *information by listing two things that individuals can do and two things that cities can do to prepare for earthquakes.*

Individuals

1. ______________________________

2. ______________________________

Cities

1. ______________________________

2. ______________________________

Name ______________________________ **Date** __________

Earthquakes and Volcanoes

Section 2 Volcanoes

PS 2.2a: The interior of Earth is hot. Heat flow and movement of material within Earth cause sections of Earth's crust to move. This may result in earthquakes, volcanic eruption, and the creation of mountains and ocean basins. **Also covered:** PS 2.2c, 2.2f

Predict *what you'll learn in this section by reading the* What You'll Learn *statements. Rewrite each statement as a question. Use these questions as a guide to the content of Section 2.*

1. ______________________________

2. ______________________________

3. ______________________________

Review Vocabulary

Define plate *to show its scientific meaning.*

plate ______________________________

____

New Vocabulary

Write the correct vocabulary term from your book next to each definition.

__________ cone-shaped hill or mountain formed when hot magma, solids, and gases erupt onto Earth's surface

__________ molten rock flowing onto Earth's surface

__________ large, broad volcano with gently sloping sides that is formed by the build up of basaltic layers

__________ relatively small volcano formed by moderate to explosive eruptions of tephra

__________ steep-sided volcano formed from alternating layers of tephra and lava

Academic Vocabulary

Read the sentence below. Use a dictionary to determine how the term factor *is being used.*

Different factors affect volcanic eruptions.

In this sentence, the word factor *means:*

factor ______________________________

____

Name ______________________________ Date ____________

Main Idea | **Details**

How do volcanoes form?

I found this information on page ______.

Sequence *the events that result in volcanic eruptions where plates collide by filling in the blanks below.*

1. An older, denser plate ____________________ a less dense plate.
2. Rock in and above the sinking plate ______________.
3. ____________________ form.
4. The magma ______________ to form ______________.

Forms of Volcanoes

I found this information on page ______.

Analyze *the way silica content helps determine how a volcano erupts to complete the following chart.*

How the composition of magma affects eruptions		
	High silica	Low silica
Consistency and flow		
Eruption		

I found this information on page ______.

Model *the 3 types of volcanoes by drawing a cross-section of each in the boxes on this page and the next. To the right of each drawing, write a caption that includes*

- how this type of volcano forms
- what this type of volcano is made of

Shield volcano

____

____

____

____

____

____

Name ______________________ Date ____________

Main Idea **Details**

Cinder cone volcano

Composite volcano

I found this information on page ______.

Describe *a* fissure eruption, *and give an example.*

CONNECT IT What type of volcano do you think appears most in the news? Why? Identify any real-life volcanoes you have heard about.

Name ______________________ Date ________

Earthquakes and Volcanoes

Section 3 Earthquakes, Volcanoes, and Plate Tectonics

PS 2.2a: The interior of Earth is hot. Heat flow and movement of material within Earth cause sections of Earth's crust to move. This may result in earthquakes, volcanic eruption, and the creation of mountains and ocean basins. **Also covered:** PS 2.2e, 2.2f

Skim *Section 3. Predict three things that you will learn.*

1. ______________________
2. ______________________
3. ______________________

Review Vocabulary

Define asthenosphere, *then use a dictionary to break down the word into its two parts and give the meaning of each part.*

asthenosphere ______________________

asthenes: ______________________

sphere: ______________________

New Vocabulary

Find the definitions of rift *and* hot spot *in your book. Then locate another sentence in the section that uses these terms and write it in the space below.*

rift Definition: ______________________

Sentence: ______________________

hot spot Definition: ______________________

Sentence: ______________________

Academic Vocabulary

Use a dictionary to define occur.

occur ______________________

Name ______________________ Date ______

Main Idea

Details

Earth's Moving Plates

I found this information on page ______.

Model *the plates of Earth's lithosphere that contribute to earthquake and volcanic activity in North America. Draw a simple map of North America and its plate and the boundaries with the plates that surround it. Label the plates.*

Where Volcanoes Form

I found this information on page ______.

Organize *information about where volcanoes form by completing the concept map.*

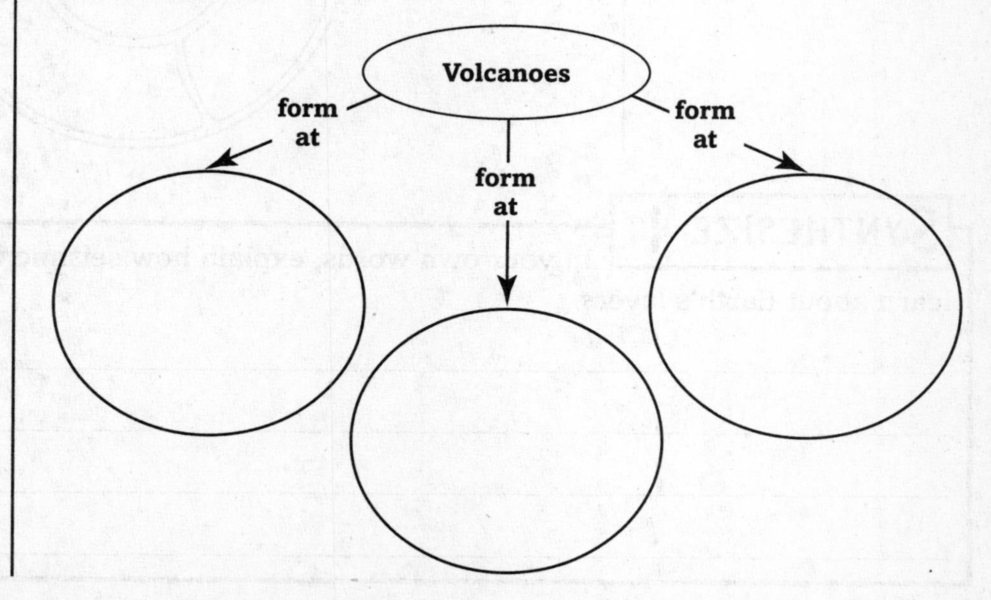

Main Idea | **Details**

Moving Plates Cause Earthquakes

I found this information on page ______.

Identify *three places where earthquakes frequently occur.*

1. ______________________
2. ______________________
3. ______________________

I found this information on page ______.

Model *what drives Earth's plates.*

- In the diagram below, label Earth's core and mantle.
- Draw three convection currents. Use arrows to show the direction of flow.
- Show a convergent boundary between two currents and a divergent boundary between two currents.

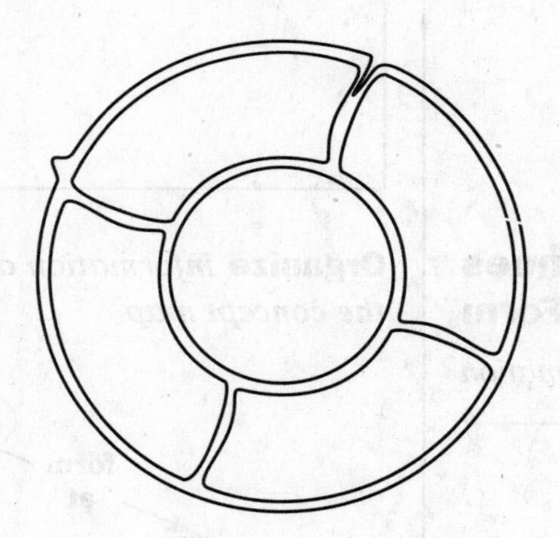

SYNTHESIZE IT

In your own words, explain how seismic waves help scientists learn about Earth's layers.

____

____

____

____

Name ____________________ Date ____________

Tie It Together

Summarize

Create a concept map or other diagram to connect concepts you have learned about volcanoes and earthquakes. Include information about

- why they occur
- how they affect humans
- how scientists measure and observe them
- what scientists know about them.

Name ______________________ Date __________

Earthquakes and Volcanoes

Chapter Wrap-Up

Review the ideas that you listed in the chart at the beginning of the chapter. Cross out any incorrect information in the first column. Then complete the chart by filling in the third column.

K What I know	W What I want to learn	L What I learned

Review

Use this checklist to help you study.

- ☐ Review the information you included in your Foldable.
- ☐ Study your *Science Notebook* on this chapter.
- ☐ Study the definitions of vocabulary words.
- ☐ Review daily homework assignments.
- ☐ Re-read the chapter and review the charts, graphs, and illustrations.
- ☐ Review the Self Check at the end of each section.
- ☐ Look over the Chapter Review at the end of the chapter.

SUMMARIZE IT **After reading this chapter, identify three things that you have learned about earthquakes and volcanoes.**

____

____

____

____

Name ______________________ Date ______________

Waves, Sound, and Light

Before You Read

Before you read the chapter, respond to these statements.

1. Write an **A** if you agree with the statement.
2. Write a **D** if you disagree with the statement.

Before You Read	Waves, Sound, and Light
	• Waves carry both matter and energy.
	• Waves occur only in water.
	• Sound travels at the same speed through all materials.
	• Light does not require matter to move through.

Construct the Foldable as directed at the beginning of this chapter.

Science Journal

Write a short paragraph describing water waves you have seen.

Name ______________________________ Date ____________

Waves, Sound, and Light

Section 1 Waves

PS 4.4c: Vibrations in materials set up wave-like disturbances that spread away from the source.
Also covered: PS 4.4a, 4.4b

Skim *Section 1 in your book. Write three questions that come to mind from what you have skimmed.*

1. ______________________________

2. ______________________________

3. ______________________________

Review Vocabulary

density

Define density *using your book or a dictionary.*

____

New Vocabulary

Write the correct vocabulary term next to its definition.

____________ distance between one point on a wave and the nearest point moving with the same speed and direction

____________ wave that causes particles in matter to move at right angles to the direction the wave travels

____________ angle an incoming wave makes with the normal equals angle the reflected wave makes with the normal

____________ disturbance that moves through matter or space and carries energy

____________ change in direction of a wave when it changes speed as it travels from one material to another

____________ number of wavelengths that pass a given point in one second, measured in hertz

____________ wave that causes particles in matter to move back and forth along the direction the wave travels

____________ bending of waves around an object

Academic Vocabulary

adjacent

Use a dictionary to define adjacent.

____

Name ______________________ Date ____________

Main Idea | **Details**

What are waves?

I found this information on page ________.

Contrast *mechanical and electromagnetic waves. Fill in the missing words.*

Mechanical waves travel through ______________. They may be ______________ waves or ______________ waves. Electromagnetic waves travel through ______________ or ______________. They are always ______________ waves.

Types of Waves

I found this information on page ________.

Create *drawings of a transverse wave and a compressional wave. Label a* trough, *a* crest, *a* compression, *and a* rarefaction.

Transverse wave
Compressional wave

Properties of Waves

I found this information on page ________.

Compare and contrast *the properties of* transverse *and* compressional waves *by defining the wave characteristics for each.*

Property	Wave Type	
	Transverse	Compressional
Wavelength		
Frequency		
Amplitude		

Name ______________________ Date ____________

Main Idea — Details

Properties of Waves

I found this information on page ______.

Complete *the equation for wave speed. Then rewrite the equation using the correct symbols.*

wave speed (m/s) = ____________ (m) × ____________ (Hz)

Wave Speed Equation ____________

Waves Can Change Directions

I found this information on page ______.

Model *the ways waves change direction by drawing examples using light waves in the boxes below.*

Light Waves Change Direction		
Reflection	Refraction	Diffraction

SUMMARIZE IT

Create, label, and describe a water wave. Identify its wavelength, frequency, and amplitude. Draw what would happen if the wave is reflected, refracted, and diffracted.

Water Wave	Refracted Wave
Reflected Wave	Diffracted Wave

Name ______________________ Date ____________

Waves, Sound, and Light

Section 2 Sound Waves

PS 4.4c: Vibrations in materials set up wave-like disturbances that spread away from the source. Sound waves are an example. Vibrational waves move at different speeds in different materials.

Scan *Section 2 of your book using the checklist below.*

- ☐ Read all section titles.
- ☐ Read all bold words.
- ☐ Read all charts and graphs.
- ☐ Look at the pictures.
- ☐ Think about what you already know about sound waves.

Write three facts you discovered about sound waves as you scanned the section.

1. ______________________
2. ______________________
3. ______________________

Review Vocabulary **Define** perception *using a dictionary or your book.*

perception ______________________

New Vocabulary *Write a sentence using the scientific meaning of each of the vocabulary words.*

intensity ______________________

pitch ______________________

reverberation ______________________

Academic Vocabulary *Use a dictionary to define* perceive.

perceive ______________________

Name ______________________ Date __________

Main Idea | **Details**

Making Sound Waves

I found this information on page ________.

Organize *the features of sound waves in the chart below.*

Properties of Sound Waves	
Produced by	
Type of wave	
How they transfer energy	

Speed of Sound

I found this information on page ________.

Identify *2 factors that affect the speed of sound.*

1. ______________________

2. ______________________

The Loudness of Sound

I found this information on page ________.

Model *Draw and label arrows to show whether* intensity, *loudness, and energy increase or decrease as the amplitude of a sound wave increases.*

Amplitude increases

Intensity ________

Loudness ________

Energy ________

Frequency and Pitch

I found this information on page ________.

Describe *the relationship between* frequency *and* pitch.

____

____

____

Name ______________________________ Date ____________

Main Idea **Details**

Hearing and the Ear

I found this information on page ______.

Sequence *the path of sound through the ear by completing the flowchart with the function and main structures of each part of the ear.*

Outer Ear

Function: ______________________________

Main Structures: ______________________________

↓

Middle Ear

Function: ______________________________

Main Structures: ______________________________

↓

Inner Ear

Function: ______________________________

Main Structures: ______________________________

The Reflection of Sound

I found this information on page ______.

Distinguish *two uses of reflected sound.*

1. ______________________________
2. ______________________________

CONNECT IT Sound in an empty room can be very loud, with many echoes. Describe three ways to make the room quieter.

____

____

____

____

____

____

Name ______________________ Date __________

Waves, Sound, and Light

Section 3 Light

PS 4.4a: Different forms of electromagnetic energy have different wavelengths. Some examples of electromagnetic energy are microwaves, infrared light, visible light, ultraviolet light, X-rays, and gamma rays.
Also covered: PS 4.4b

Predict *three things that might be discussed in Section 3. Read the section headings and subheadings to help make your predictions.*

1. ______________________
2. ______________________
3. ______________________

Review Vocabulary

Define spectrum *and use it in a sentence.*

spectrum ______________________

New Vocabulary

Use your book to define each of the new vocabulary terms.

electromagnetic waves ______________________

electromagnetic spectrum ______________________

infrared waves ______________________

ultraviolet waves ______________________

Academic Vocabulary

Use a dictionary to define interact.

interact ______________________

Name ______________________________ Date __________

Main Idea | **Details**

Waves in Empty Space

I found this information on page ____________.

Analyze *why light travels faster in empty space than when it travels through matter.*

____

____

____

Properties of Light Waves

I found this information on page ____________.

Model *an electromagnetic wave. Draw and label both the electric and the magnetic fields, and indicate the wavelength and the direction of travel.*

The Electromagnetic Spectrum

I found this information on page ____________.

Organize *information about the uses of electromagnetic waves.*

Wave Type	Used For
radio waves	
microwaves	
infrared waves	
visible light	
ultraviolet waves	
X rays	
gamma rays	

Main Idea | **Details**

The Eye and Seeing Light

I found this information on page ________.

Sequence *the path of light through the eye and organize the structures involved at each step.*

Light enters eye
Main Structures:
____

→ **Light waves are focused**
Main Structures:
____

→ **Image formed**
Main Structures:
____

→ **Carries messages to brain**
Main Structures:
____

I found this information on page ________.

Summarize *what determines the color of objects that emit light and what determines the color of objects that do not.*

____

____

____

____

Contrast *the roles of rods and cones. Complete the chart.*

Cell	Sensitive to:
rod	
cone	

SYNTHESIZE IT Think of a source of electromagnetic waves, such as a radio station or a microwave oven. Describe the waves given off by the source, including their wavelength and frequency.

____

____

____

Name ______________________ Date __________

Tie It Together

Identify ways that sound waves, visible light waves, and other types of electromagnetic waves play a role in your daily life. For each type of wave, give an example of when the waves are useful. Identify any problems the waves can cause.

Sound Waves

Visible Light

Other Types of Electromagnetic Waves

Name ______________________________ Date ______________

Waves, Sound, and Light

Chapter Wrap-Up

Now that you have read the chapter, think about what you have learned and complete the chart below. Compare your previous answers with these.

1. Write an **A** if you agree with the statement.
2. Write a **D** if you disagree with the statement.

Waves, Sound, and Light	After You Read
• Waves carry both matter and energy.	
• Waves occur only in water.	
• Sound travels at the same speed through all materials.	
• Light does not require matter to move through.	

Review

Use this checklist to help you study.

- ☐ Review the information you included in your Foldable.
- ☐ Study your *Science Notebook* on this chapter.
- ☐ Study the definitions of vocabulary words.
- ☐ Review daily homework assignments.
- ☐ Re-read the chapter and review the charts, graphs, and illustrations.
- ☐ Review the Self Check at the end of each section.
- ☐ Look over the Chapter Review at the end of the chapter.

SUMMARIZE IT **After reading this chapter, identify three things that you have learned about waves, sound, and light.**

____

____

____

Name ______________________________ Date __________

Matter and Its Changes

Before You Read

Preview the chapter title, section titles, and section headings. Complete the chart by listing at least two ideas for each section in each column.

K What I know	W What I want to find out

FOLDABLES™ Study Organizer *Construct the Foldable as directed at the beginning of this chapter.*

Science Journal

Wendy Craig Duncan carried the Olympic flame underwater on the way to the 2000 Summer Olympics in Sydney, Australia. How many different states of matter do you think would be involved in this task? List as many as you can.

Name ______________________ **Date** ____________

Matter and Its Changes

Section 1 Physical Properties and Changes

PS 3.1c: The motion of particles helps to explain the phases (states) of matter as well as changes from one phase to another. **3.1g:** Characteristic properties can be used to identify different materials, and separate a mixture of substances into its components. **Also covered:** PS 3.1a, 3.1d, 3.1e, 3.1f, 3.2a

Scan *Section 1 of your book. Write a sentence about physical properties of matter.*

____

____

Review Vocabulary **Define** mass *to show its scientific meaning.*

mass ______________________

New Vocabulary *Use your book to write a definition for each word listed below.*

matter ______________________

____

physical change ______________________

____

density ______________________

____

states of matter ______________________

____

melting point ______________________

____

boiling point ______________________

____

Academic Vocabulary *Use your book or a dictionary to define* identify.

identify ______________________

____

Name ______________________ Date ________

Main Idea | **Details**

Using Your Senses

I found this information on page ______.

Create *a drawing below to represent the senses you use for making observations. Label each drawing with the sense it represents. Identify those senses that should not be used in the lab.*

Physical Properties

I found this information on page ______.

Complete *the statement below about physical properties.*

Physical Properties of a material can be ______________________

____

Physical Properties you observe include

1. ______________ 3. ______________

2. ______________

Physical Properties you can measure include

1. ______________ 3. ______________

2. ______________ 4. ______________

States of Matter

I found this information on page ______.

Sequence *the four states of matter of any substance according to its temperature by completing the blanks.*

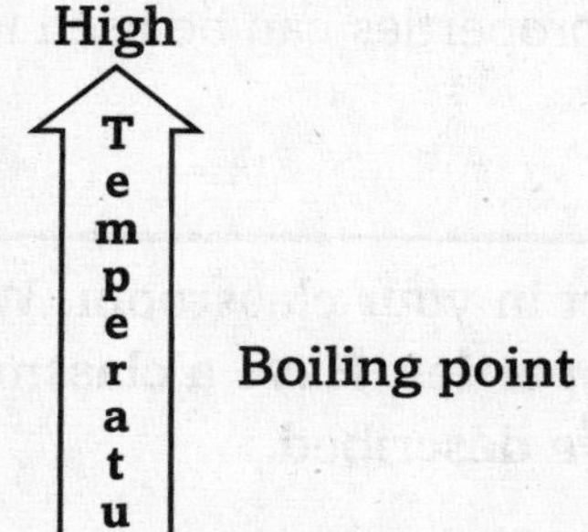

1. ______________

2. ______________

3. ______________

4. ______________

Name ______________________________ Date __________

Main Idea | **Details**

Metallic Properties

I found this information on page ______.

Organize *the information on metallic properties below. Each circle should include a metallic property and a description of the property. The first one has been done for you.*

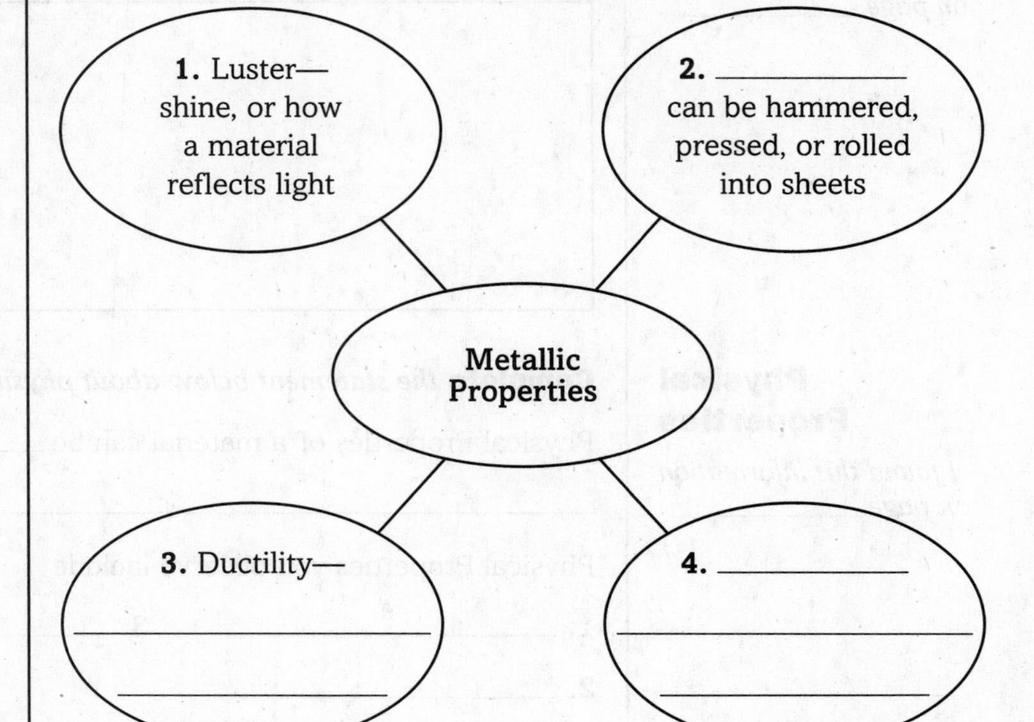

Using Physical Properties

I found this information on page ______.

Summarize *three ways that you can use the physical properties of substances by completing the blanks in the sentences below.*

1. Physical properties can be used to ______________ substances.
2. Physical properties can be used to ______________ substances.
3. Physical properties can be used to ______________ substances.

CONNECT IT Choose an object in your classroom. Write a creative description of the object, using only physical properties. Have a classmate read your description and try to identify the object you have described.

____

____

Name ______________________________ Date __________

Matter and Its Changes

Section 2 Chemical Properties and Changes

PS 3.1a: Substances have characteristic properties. **3.2c:** During a chemical change, substances react in characteristic ways to form new substances with different physical and chemical properties.
Also covered: PS 3.1g, 3.2e

Scan *the title and headings in Section 2. Predict three things that might be discussed in this section.*

1. ______________________________
2. ______________________________
3. ______________________________

Review Vocabulary

Define *the word* heat *as it relates to the states of matter. Use your book or a dictionary for help.*

heat ______________________________

New Vocabulary

Use each of the words below in an original sentence that reflects the word's scientific meaning.

chemical property ______________________________

chemical change ______________________________

law of conservation of mass ______________________________

Academic Vocabulary

Use a dictionary to find the scientific meaning of react.

react ______________________________

Ability to Change

I found this information on page __________.

Contrast *physical properties and chemical properties. Write a summary of the differences between these properties.*

____

Name ______________________ Date __________

Main Idea | **Details**

Common Chemical Properties

I found this information on page ______.

Complete *the chart as you read the section. The left column lists common chemical properties. The right column gives an example of that property. The first row of the chart has been done for you.*

Type of Chemical Property	Example
Flammability	Wood will burn.
Reacts with oxygen	
	Silver can tarnish.
	A vitamin can change to another substance.
Reacts when heated or cooled	
	Water breaks down, or decomposes.

Something New

I found this information on page ______.

Identify *six signs that a chemical change has occurred.*

1. ______
2. ______
3. ______
4. ______
5. ______
6. ______

Name ______________________ Date __________

Main Idea | **Details**

Something New

I found this information on page ________.

Compare and contrast *chemical changes and physical changes by completing the Venn diagram with at least five facts.*

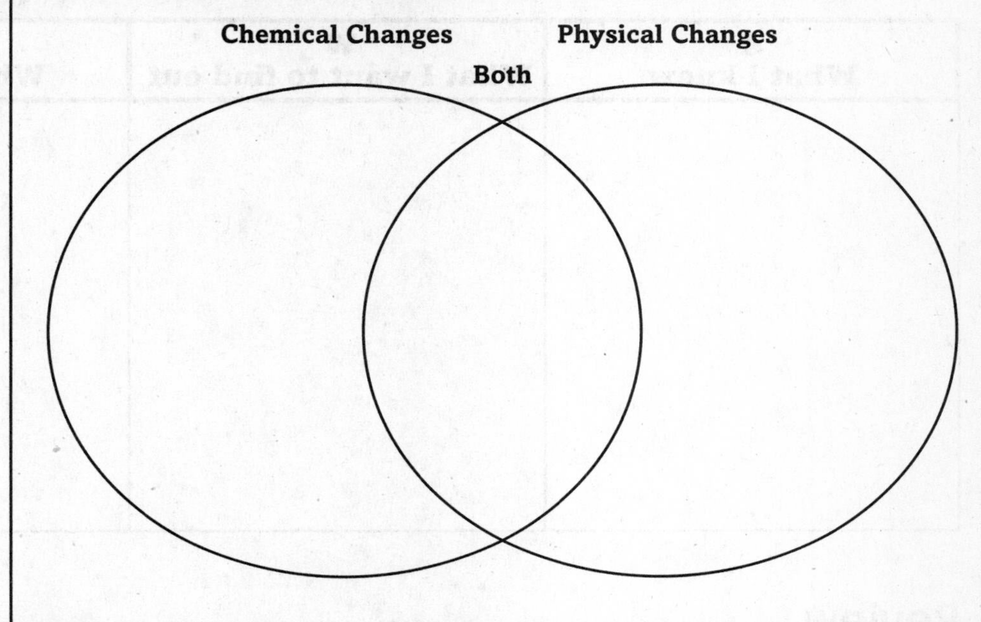

The Law of Conservation of Mass

I found this information on page ________.

Create *a diagram of a campfire below. Label your drawing to show the chemical change that is occurring and how mass is conserved.*

CONNECT IT

Give two examples of how understanding chemical properties can be useful in your daily life.

1. ______________________________

____

2. ______________________________

____

Name ______________________________ Date __________

Matter and Its Changes Chapter Wrap-Up

Review the ideas you listed in the chart at the beginning of the chapter. Cross out any incorrect information in the first column. Then complete the chart by filling in the third column.

K What I know	W What I want to find out	L What I learned

Review

Use this checklist to help you study.

- ☐ Review the information you included in your Foldable.
- ☐ Study your *Science Notebook* on this chapter.
- ☐ Study the definitions of vocabulary words.
- ☐ Review daily homework assignments.
- ☐ Re-read the chapter and review the charts, graphs, and illustrations.
- ☐ Review the Self Check at the end of each section.
- ☐ Look over the Chapter Review at the end of the chapter.

SUMMARIZE IT **After reading this chapter, identify three things that you have learned about matter and how it changes.**

____

____

____

Name ______________________ Date ______________

Atoms, Elements, and the Periodic Table

Before You Read

Preview the chapter title, section titles, and the section headings. List at least two ideas for each section in each column.

K What I know	W What I want to find out

Construct the Foldable as directed at the beginning of this chapter.

Science Journal

Make a list of three questions that you think of when you see hot air balloons.

____

____

____

____

____

____

____

Name ______________________ Date ____________

Atoms, Elements, and the Periodic Table

PS 3.3a: All matter is made up of atoms. Atoms are far too small to see with a light microscope.
Also covered: PS 3.3b, 3.3c

Section 1 Structure of Matter

Read *the* What You'll Learn *statements for Section 1. Write three questions that come to mind. Look for answers to each question as you read the section.*

1. ______________________
2. ______________________
3. ______________________

Review Vocabulary

Define density *to show its scientific meaning.*

density ______________________

New Vocabulary

Write the correct vocabulary word next to each definition.

__________ small particle that makes up most kinds of matter

__________ uncharged particle in the nucleus of an atom

__________ invisible, negatively charged particle

__________ anything that has mass and takes up space

__________ statement that matter is not created or destroyed, but only changes its form

__________ positively charged central part of an atom

__________ positively charged particle in the nucleus of an atom

Academic Vocabulary

Use a dictionary to define **theory.**

theory ______________________

____

Name ______________________________ Date ______________

Main Idea	Details
What is matter? What isn't matter? *I found this information on page* ______.	**State** *the two characteristics common to all* matter. 1. ______________________________ 2. ______________________________ **Label** *each example as* matter *or* not matter. air ____________ light ____________ heat ____________ water ____________
What makes up matter? *I found this information on page* ______.	**Organize** *Democritus's ideas about* atoms. *Complete the concept map.*

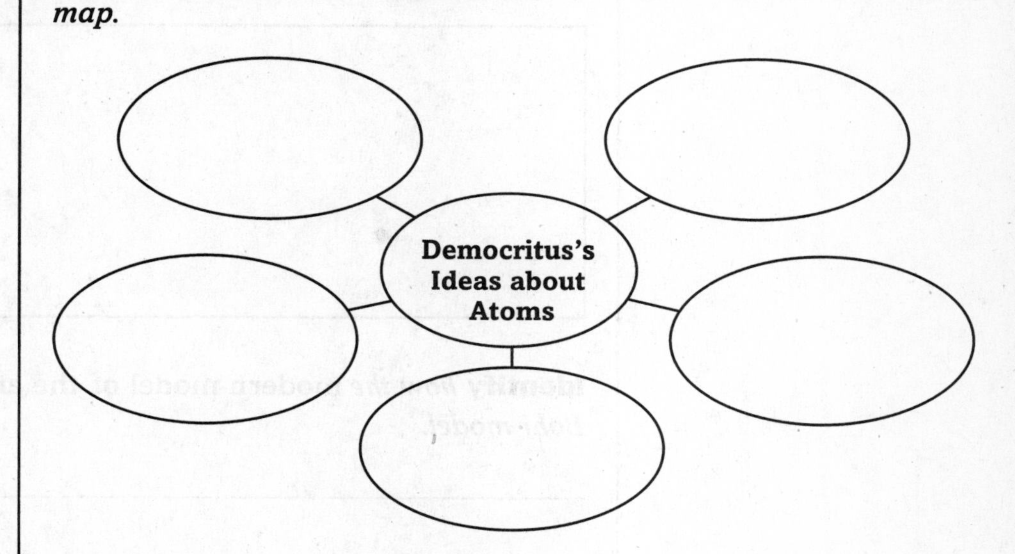

Identify *the two main ideas in* Dalton's atomic theory of matter.

1. ______________________________
2. ______________________________

Summarize Lavoisier's experiment *and the conclusion he drew from it.*

Experiment:	→	Conclusion:

Name _______________ Date _______________

Main Idea | **Details**

Models of the Atom

I found this information on page ______.

Compare and contrast *the* Thomson *and* Rutherford atomic models.

____

____

____

____

I found this information on page ______.

Create *a drawing of the* Bohr atom. *Label the* positively charged, negatively charged, *and* neutral parts.

Identify *how the* modern model of the atom *differs from the Bohr model.*

____

____

ANALYZE IT

Make a relative time line of atomic models. List the models from oldest to youngest. State the new discovery that was made with the development of each new model.

Name ______________________ Date ____________

Atoms, Elements, and the Periodic Table

PS 3.3f: There are more than 100 elements. Elements combine in a multitude of ways to produce compounds that account for all living and nonliving substances. **3.3g:** The periodic table is one useful model for classifying elements. **Also covered:** PS 3.2d, 3.3e

Section 2 The Simplest Matter

Skim *the headings and subheadings in Section 2. Write three predictions about what you will learn in this section.*

1. ______________________
2. ______________________
3. ______________________

Review Vocabulary *Write a scientific sentence using the word* mass.

mass ______________________

____

New Vocabulary *Write the correct vocabulary term next to each definition.*

______________ matter made of only one kind of atom

______________ number of protons in the nucleus of each atom of an element

______________ atom of an element with a different number of neutrons

______________ the number of protons plus the number of neutrons in an atom

______________ weighted average mass of the isotopes of an element

______________ element that generally has a shiny luster and is a good conductor of heat and electricity

______________ element that is usually dull in appearance and is a poor conductor of heat and electricity

______________ element that has characteristics of metals and nonmetals

Academic Vocabulary **Define** unique *using a dictionary.*

unique ______________________

____

Name ______________________________ Date ______________

Main Idea | **Details**

The Elements

I found this information on page ________.

Summarize *three key facts about* elements.

1. ______________________________
2. ______________________________
3. ______________________________

The Periodic Table

I found this information on page ________.

Complete *the graphic organizer to show how the* periodic table *is organized.*

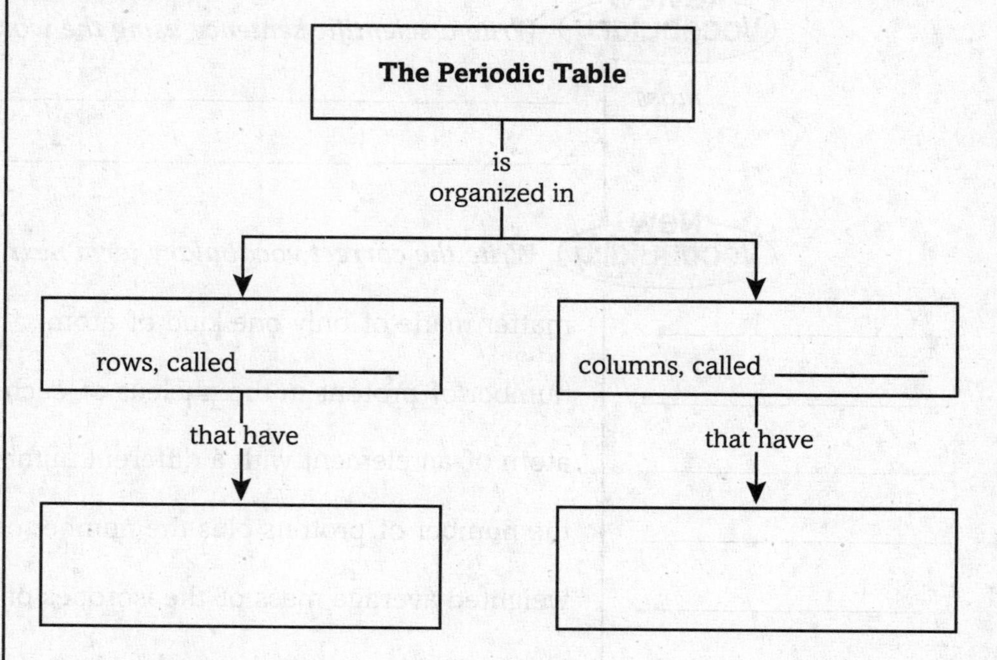

Identifying Characteristics

I found this information on page ________.

Label *the square below with information you would find about chlorine on the periodic table. Identify each piece of information and explain what you can learn from it.*

Name ______________________ Date ____________

Main Idea | **Details**

Identifying Characteristics

I found this information on page ______.

Contrast *the three* isotopes *of hydrogen. Complete the chart.*

Isotope	Protium	Deuterium	Tritium
Number of protons			
Number of neutrons			
Mass number			

Classification of Elements

I found this information on page ______.

Summarize *the four characteristics of each type of element in the chart below.*

Metals	Nonmetals	Metalloids
1.		
2.		
3.		
4.		

SYNTHESIZE IT

Metals, nonmetals, and metalloids are located in specific areas of the periodic table. Use what you know about elements and the periodic table to explain why this is.

____

____

____

____

Name ______________________ Date __________

Atoms, Elements, and the Periodic Table

Section 3 Compounds and Mixtures

PS 3.2b: Mixtures are physical combinations of materials and can be separated by physical means. **3.3f:** There are more than 100 elements. Elements combine in a multitude of ways to produce compounds that account for all living and nonliving substances.
Also covered: PS 3.1g, 3.3g

Scan *Section 3 using the checklist below.*

- ☐ Read all section headings.
- ☐ Read all bold words.
- ☐ Read all charts and graphs.
- ☐ Look at the pictures.
- ☐ Think about what you already know about compounds and mixtures.

Write two facts you learned about compounds and mixtures as you scanned the section.

1. ______________________

2. ______________________

Review Vocabulary

Define formula. *Then use the term in an original sentence to show its scientific meaning.*

formula ______________________

New Vocabulary

Use each vocabulary term in a scientific sentence.

substance ______________________

compound ______________________

mixture ______________________

Academic Vocabulary

Use a dictionary to define symbol. *Give an example of a symbol you have used in science.*

symbol ______________________

Name ______________________ Date ____________

Main Idea **Details**

Substances

I found this information on page ________.

Classify *the types of* substances. *Complete the graphic organizer by describing each type and giving two examples.*

Substances

Type: ________	**Type:** ________
Description: ________	**Description:** ________
Examples: ________	**Examples:** ________

I found this information on page ________.

Summarize *what information is contained in the formula of a* **compound.**

____

Analyze *the formula of each compound. Identify which elements are in each compound and how many atoms of each element make up one unit of the compound.*

	Water	**Hydrogen peroxide**	**Carbon dioxide**	**Carbon monoxide**
Formula	H_2O	H_2O_2	CO_2	CO
Atoms and elements				

Name ______________________________ Date ____________

Main Idea | **Details**

Mixtures

I found this information on page ________.

Contrast compounds *and* mixtures. *Complete the Venn diagram with at least five facts.*

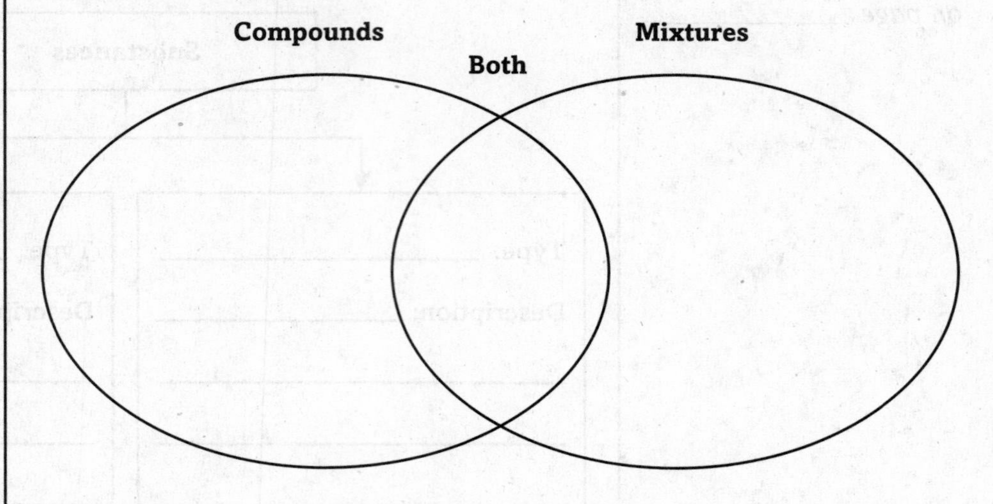

I found this information on page ________.

Summarize *characteristics of* homogeneous *and* heterogeneous mixtures.

A homogeneous mixture ______________________________.

You __________ see the individual parts. A heterogeneous mixture

____.

You __________ see the individual parts.

Examples of a homogeneous mixture: ______________________

____

Examples of a heterogeneous mixture: ______________________

____

CONNECT IT Give examples of two mixtures and two compounds that are important to your everyday life.

____

____

____

Name ______________________ Date __________

Tie It Together

The formulas for three substances are listed below.

- ***Describe the properties of each substance as thoroughly as you can.***
- ***Identify each as an element or a compound.***
- ***Write the number of protons in the nuclei of the element or elements in each substance.***
- ***State whether those elements are metals, nonmetals, or metalloids, and any properties you can infer for those elements.***
- ***Use a periodic table.***

1. Water (H_2O): ______________________________

2. Table salt (NaCl): ______________________________

3. Gold (Au): ______________________________

Name ______________________________ Date __________

Atoms, Elements, and the Periodic Table Chapter Wrap-Up

Review the ideas you listed in the chart at the beginning of the chapter. Cross out any incorrect information in the first column. Then complete the chart by filling in the third column. How do your ideas now compare with those you provided at the beginning of the chapter?

K What I know	W What I want to find out	L What I learned

Review

Use this checklist to help you study.

- ☐ Review the information you included in your Foldable.
- ☐ Study your *Science Notebook* on this chapter.
- ☐ Study the definitions of vocabulary words.
- ☐ Review daily homework assignments.
- ☐ Re-read the chapter and review the charts, graphs, and illustrations.
- ☐ Review the Self Check at the end of each section.
- ☐ Look over the Chapter Review at the end of the chapter.

SUMMARIZE IT **After reading this chapter, identify three things that you have learned about atoms and elements.**

____

____

____

____

Name ______________________________ Date ______________

Substances, Mixtures, and Solubility

Before You Read

Before you read the chapter, respond to these statements.

1. Write an **A** if you agree with the statement.
2. Write a **D** if you disagree with the statement.

Before You Read	Substances, Mixtures, and Solubility
	• Burning a substance changes it into other substances.
	• All mixtures are solutions.
	• Stirring can speed up the rate at which a substance dissolves.
	• Acidic foods are sour.

Construct the Foldable as directed at the beginning of this chapter.

Science Journal

Find and name four items around you that are mixtures.

Name ______________________ Date __________

Substances, Mixtures, and Solubility

Section 1 What is a solution?

PS 3.1a: Substances have characteristic properties. Some of these properties include color, odor, phase at room temperature, density, solubility, heat and electrical conductivity, hardness, and boiling and freezing points. **Also covered:** PS 3.1g, 3.3f

Read *the* What You'll Learn *statements for Section 1. Write four questions you have after reading the statements.*

1. ______________________
2. ______________________
3. ______________________
4. ______________________

Review Vocabulary

Define proton *to show its scientific meaning.*

proton ______________________

New Vocabulary

Write the correct vocabulary word in the left column next to each definition.

______ solid that comes out of its solution due to a chemical reaction

______ matter with the same composition and properties throughout

______ substance that dissolves a solute

______ mixture in which substances are not evenly mixed

______ mixture with two or more substances that are evenly mixed

______ substance that dissolves and seems to disappear into another substance

______ another name for a homogeneous mixture

Academic Vocabulary

Use a dictionary to define **proportion** *to show its scientific meaning.*

proportion ______________________

Name ______________________________ Date ____________

Main Idea — Details

Substances

I found this information on page ______.

Compare elements *and* compounds *by completing the chart.*

Substance	Definition
Element	
Compound	

I found this information on page ______.

Contrast physical *and* chemical processes. *Complete the sentences.*

Physical processes ________ change substances.

Chemical processes ________ change substances.

Mixtures

I found this information on page ______.

Distinguish heterogeneous *and* homogeneous mixtures. *Place the phrases in the Venn diagram.*

- not bonded chemically
- not evenly mixed
- evenly mixed
- can be physically separated
- also known as solutions

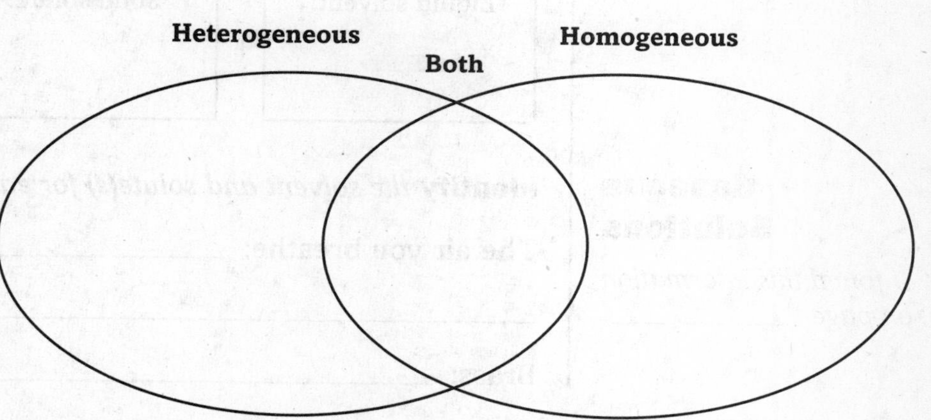

How Solutions Form

I found this information on page ______.

Summarize *how* solutions *form. Define* solute *and* solvent *in your answer.*

____

____

____

____

Name ______________________ Date __________

Main Idea — Details

I found this information on page ______.

Contrast crystallization *and* precipitate formation.

Crystallization: ______________________

Precipitate formation: ______________________

Liquid Solutions

I found this information on page ______.

Organize *examples of each type of solution.*

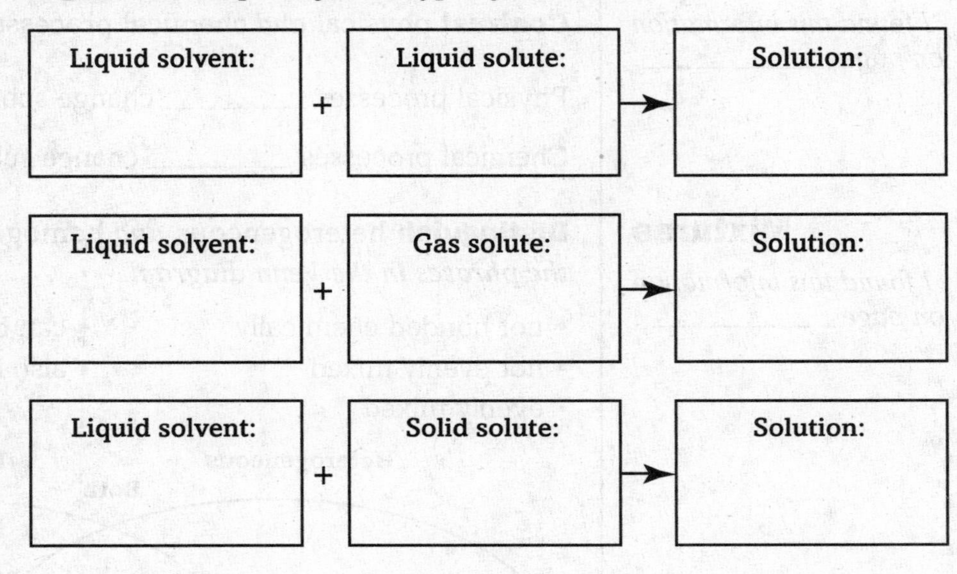

Gaseous Solutions

I found this information on page ______.

Identify *the solvent and solute(s) for each solution.*

The air you breathe: ______________________

Brass: ______________________

CONNECT IT

A jar of ocean water sits on a shelf uncovered for some time. Once the water is gone, a white, salty substance is left in the jar. Hypothesize what kind of change occurred. What does this tell you about the water?

____

Name ______________________________ Date ______________

Substances, Mixtures, and Solubility

Section 2 Solubility

PS 3.1b: Solubility can be affected by the nature of the solute and solvent, temperature, and pressure. The rate of solution can be affected by the size of the particles, stirring, temperature, and the amount of solute already dissolved. **Also covered:** PS 4.2e

Scan *the headings, bold words, and illustrations in Section 2. Write two facts you learned as you scanned the section.*

1. ______________________________

2. ______________________________

Review Vocabulary

Define polar bond.

polar bond ______________________________

New Vocabulary

Write a scientific definition for each vocabulary term.

aqueous ______________________________

solubility ______________________________

saturated ______________________________

concentration ______________________________

Academic Vocabulary

Use a dictionary to define chemical *as an adjective.*

chemical ______________________________

Name ______________________ Date ____________

Main Idea | **Details**

Water—The Universal Solvent

I found this information on page ________.

Model and label *a* water molecule, *including:*

- the shared electrons in the bonds
- the partial positive and partial negative charge areas
- the hydrogen and oxygen atoms

I found this information on page ________.

Contrast *the ways in which* ionic *and* polar molecular compounds *dissolve in water. Complete the chart.*

Type of Compound	How It Dissolves in Water
Ionic	
Polar molecular	

What will dissolve?

I found this information on page ________.

Analyze *the phrase "like dissolves like." Summarize what this phrase means in your own words.*

____

____

____

Name ______________________ Date __________

Main Idea	Details
How much will dissolve? *I found this information on page* ______.	**Summarize** *how temperature affects* solubility. As temperature increases, the solubility of liquid-solid solutions usually __________ and the solubility of liquid-gas solutions usually __________. **Describe** *a* saturated solution *and tell how a solution can become* supersaturated. ______ ______ ______ ______ ______
Rate of Dissolving *I found this information on page* ______.	**Identify** *three ways the rate of dissolving can be increased.* 1. ______ 2. ______ 3. ______
Concentration *I found this information on page* ______.	**Summarize** *how adding solute changes the properties of a solvent.* ______ ______

SUMMARIZE IT A chef slowly stirs sugar into a pot of water. Describe what happens to the solution as the water heats. What can you conclude about how long it will take the solution to boil?

______

______

______

Name ______________________ Date __________

Substances, Mixtures, and Solubility

Section 3 Acidic and Basic Solutions

PS 3.1a: Substances have characteristic properties. Some of these properties include color, odor, phase at room temperature, density, solubility, heat and electrical conductivity, hardness, and boiling and freezing points.

Predict *three topics you expect to be discussed in Section 3. Read the headings and bold words to help make your prediction.*

1. ______________________
2. ______________________
3. ______________________

Review Vocabulary

Define physical property *using your book or a dictionary.*

physical property ______________________

New Vocabulary

Write an original sentence using each vocabulary term.

neutralization ______________________

pH ______________________

hydronium ion ______________________

base ______________________

indicator ______________________

acid ______________________

Academic Vocabulary

Use a dictionary to define conduct *as a verb in its scientific sense.*

conduct ______________________

Name ____________________ Date __________

Main Idea

Details

Acids

I found this information on page ________.

Model and label *the formation of a* hydronium ion *from a hydrogen ion in water.*

Write a sentence explaining how hydronium forms from an acid.

I found this information on page ________.

Organize *information about the properties of acids and some examples of acids. Complete the diagram.*

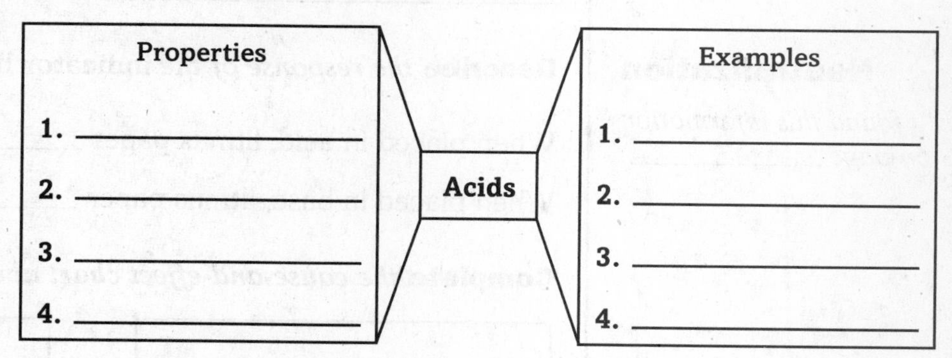

Bases

I found this information on page ________.

Organize *properties and examples of* bases. *Complete the diagram.*

Properties	Bases	Examples
1.		1.
2.		2.
3.		3.
4.		4.
5.		5.
6.		6.

Name ______________________________ Date ____________

Main Idea | **Details**

What is pH?

I found this information on page ______.

Label *the diagram of the* pH scale. *Label the areas of the scale for* acids, bases, *and* neutral *solutions. Draw arrows showing how the strength of acids and bases increases.*

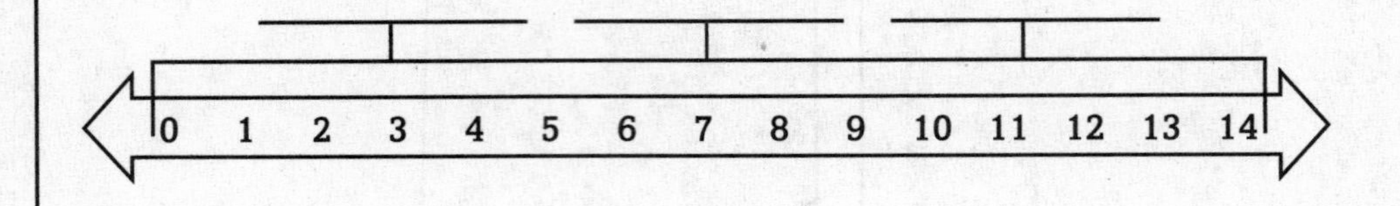

Indicators

I found this information on page ______.

Summarize *what determines the strength of acidic and basic solutions.*

____

____

____

Neutralization

I found this information on page ______.

Describe *the response of the* indicator litmus paper *in each case.*

When placed in acid, litmus paper ______________________.

When placed in base, litmus paper ______________________.

Complete *the cause-and-effect chart about* neutralization.

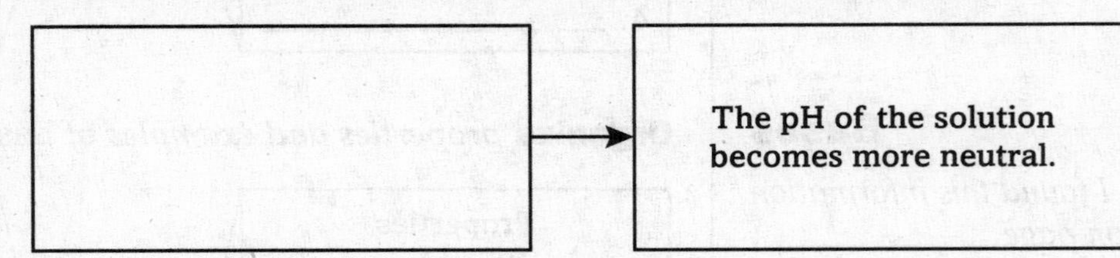

CONNECT IT Heartburn is caused by excess acid in the digestive system. Antacid tablets treat heartburn by neutralizing the acid. Explain what you can conclude about the tablets, and why.

____

____

____

Name ______________________ Date __________

Tie It Together

Can You Guess?

Write clues that a classmate could use to guess three substances or mixtures from everyday life. Include information about the properties and uses of the substance or mixture.

For example, if you chose vinegar, you might write:

"This is a liquid-liquid solution. It is a weak acid. It is used on salads and in other foods."

Trade clues with a classmate and try to guess each other's items.

1. ____

____

____

____

____

____

2. ____

____

____

____

____

____

3. ____

____

____

____

____

____

Name ______________________________ Date ____________

Substances, Mixtures, and Solubility

Chapter Wrap-Up

Now that you have read the chapter, think about what you have learned and complete the table below. Compare your previous answers with these.

1. Write an **A** if you agree with the statement.
2. Write a **D** if you disagree with the statement.

Substances, Mixtures, and Solubility	After You Read
• Burning a substance changes it into other substances.	
• All mixtures are solutions.	
• Stirring can speed up the rate at which a substance dissolves.	
• Acidic foods are sour.	

Review

Use this checklist to help you study.

- ☐ Review the information you included in your Foldable.
- ☐ Study your *Science Notebook* on this chapter.
- ☐ Study the definitions of vocabulary words.
- ☐ Review daily homework assignments.
- ☐ Re-read the chapter and review the charts, graphs, and illustrations.
- ☐ Review the Self Check at the end of each section.
- ☐ Look over the Chapter Review at the end of the chapter.

SUMMARIZE IT **After reading this chapter, identify three things that you have learned that surprised you.**

____

____

____

____

Name ______________________ Date ____________

Chemical Reactions

Before You Read

Preview the chapter title, section titles, and section headings. List at least two ideas for each section in each column.

K What I know	W What I want to find out

FOLDABLES™ Study Organizer

Construct the Foldable as directed at the beginning of this chapter.

Science Journal

What types of products do you think are manufactured in a chemical plant?

Name ______________________________ Date ______________

Chemical Reactions

Section 1 Chemical Formulas and Equations

PS 3.2c: During a chemical change, substances react in characteristic ways to form new substances with different physical and chemical properties. **Also covered:** PS 3.2d, 3.2e, 3.3d, 4.3a

Skim *Section 1 of your text. Read the headings and look at the illustrations. Write three questions that come to mind.*

1. ______________________________
2. ______________________________
3. ______________________________

Review Vocabulary **Define** atom *to show its scientific meaning.*

atom ______________________________

____

New Vocabulary *Write the correct vocabulary term next to its definition.*

______________ substance that exists before a chemical reaction begins

______________ chemical reaction that releases heat energy

______________ process that produces a chemical change

______________ chemical reaction that absorbs heat energy

______________ substance that forms as a result of a chemical reaction

______________ tells the reactants, products, physical state, and proportions of each substance in a chemical reaction

Academic Vocabulary *Use a dictionary to define* undergo.

undergo ______________________________

____

Name ______________________________ Date __________

Main Idea | **Details**

Physical or Chemical Change?

I found this information on page ________.

Compare and contrast *the two types of* changes in matter *by completing the chart.*

	Physical Change	Chemical Change
Description		
Examples		

Chemical Equations

I found this information on page ________.

Label *the* products, reactants, *and* subscripts *in the* chemical equation.

________ ________

$$CH_3COOH + NaHCO_3 \longrightarrow CH_3COONa + H_2O + CO_2$$

Conservation of Mass

I found this information on page ________.

Complete *the chart below about the* chemical reaction *above. Then summarize the* law of conservation of mass.

Element	C	H	O	Na
Number of atoms in reactants	3		5	
Number of atoms in products				

The law of conservation of mass states that ______________________________
____
____
____.

Name ______________________________ Date ____________

Main Idea | **Details**

Balancing Chemical Equations

I found this information on page ________.

Complete *the process of balancing the* chemical equation *below. First, count the number of atoms of each element in the products and the* reactants *to complete the chart.*

$CH_4 + O_2 \longrightarrow CO_2 + H_2O$

	Carbon	Hydrogen	Oxygen
Reactants			
Products			

Balance the number of hydrogen atoms in the equation by writing the correct coefficient in front of the correct molecule. Then count and record the atoms in the new equation.

$CH_4 + O_2 \longrightarrow CO_2 + \_\_\_ H_2O$

	Carbon	Hydrogen	Oxygen
Reactants			
Products			

Finish balancing the equation by balancing the number of oxygen atoms in the equation.

$CH_4 + \_\_\_ O_2 \longrightarrow CO_2 + \_\_\_ H_2O$

Energy in Chemical Reactions

I found this information on page ________.

Predict *whether the reaction above is* endothermic *or* exothermic *and explain why. The energy term would appear on the right side of the equation.*

____

COMPARE IT Compare the terms endothermic and exothermic.

____

____

____

Name ______________________ Date __________

Chemical Reactions

Section 2 Rates of Chemical Reactions

PS 3.2c: During a chemical change, substances react in characteristic ways to form new substances with different physical and chemical properties. **Also covered:** PS 3.3d, 4.3a

***Scan** the headings, bold words, and illustrations in Section 2. Write two facts that you learned as you scanned the section.*

1. ______________________

2. ______________________

Define state of matter *in a scientific sentence.*

state of matter ______________________

Write the correct vocabulary term next to its definition.

__________ substance that slows down a chemical reaction

__________ large protein molecule that speeds up a chemical reaction

__________ substance that speeds up a chemical reaction without changing permanently or being used up

__________ energy needed to start a chemical reaction

__________ amount of a substance present in a certain volume

__________ how fast a chemical reaction happens after it is started

Use a dictionary to define **volume.**

volume ______________________

Name ______________________________ Date ____________

Main Idea | **Details**

How fast? and Activation Energy—Starting a Reaction

I found this information on page ________.

Evaluate *the events that occur during a chemical reaction by completing the paragraph.*

Activation energy is the ____________ needed to start a(n) ____________. Molecules of the reactants can then ____________ with enough energy to ____________ the ____________ of the reactants. New bonds ____________ to create the products of the reaction.

Reaction Rate

I found this information on page ________.

Describe *two ways that the* **rate of a reaction** *can be measured.*

Reaction rate can be found by measuring
- ____________
- ____________

I found this information on page ________.

Complete *the concept map by identifying factors that affect* **reaction rate.**

Factors that Affect Reaction Rate

- ____________: Changing the speed and energy with which molecules collide affects the reaction rate.
- ____________: The number of reactant molecules in a given volume affects the chance that molecules will collide and react.
- ____________: Only atoms in the outer layer of the reactant material can react—the number of molecules out in the open affects reaction rate.

Name ______________________ Date __________

Main Idea | **Details**

Slowing Down Reactions

I found this information on page ______.

Summarize *the information about* inhibitors. *Include an example.*

____

____

____

____

Speeding Up Reactions

I found this information on page ______.

Complete *the graphic organizer about ways* catalysts *can work.*

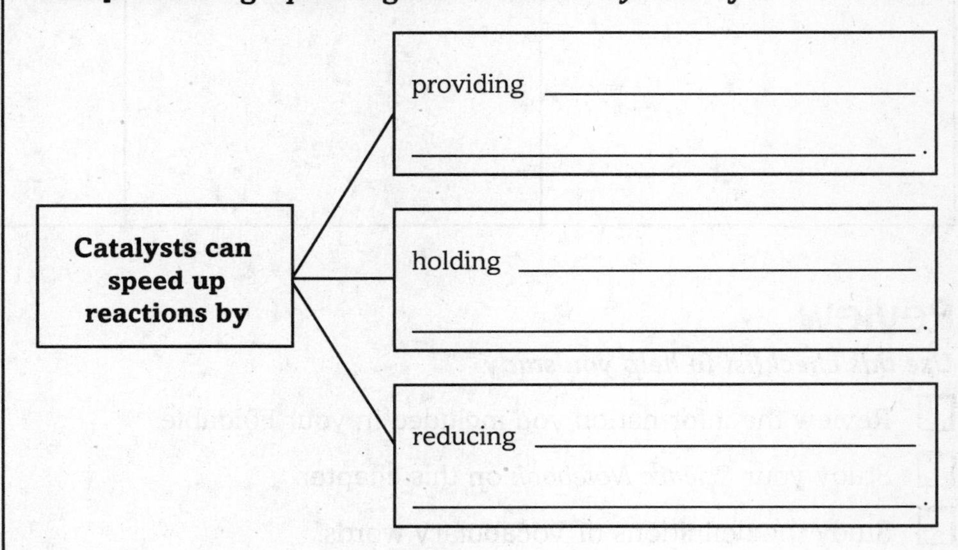

I found this information on page ______.

Identify *four other functions that* enzymes *carry out in the body.*

1. ______________________
2. ______________________
3. ______________________
4. ______________________

SYNTHESIZE IT

A scientist adds 1 mg of a catalyst to a solution to speed reaction rate. How much of the catalyst will be left after the reaction occurs? Explain.

____

____

____

Name ______________________ Date __________

Chemical Reactions Chapter Wrap-Up

Review the ideas you listed in the chart at the beginning of the chapter. Cross out any incorrect information in the first column. Then complete the chart by filling in the third column. Compare your previous responses with these.

K What I know	W What I want to find out	L What I learned

Review

Use this checklist to help you study.

- ☐ Review the information you included in your Foldable.
- ☐ Study your *Science Notebook* on this chapter.
- ☐ Study the definitions of vocabulary words.
- ☐ Review daily homework assignments.
- ☐ Re-read the chapter and review the charts, graphs, and illustrations.
- ☐ Review the Self Check at the end of each section.
- ☐ Look over the Chapter Review at the end of the chapter.

SUMMARIZE IT **After reading this chapter, identify three things that you have learned about chemical reactions.**

____

____

____

____

Name ______________________________ Date ____________

Cells—The Units of Life

Before You Read

Before you read the chapter, respond to these statements.

1. Write an **A** if you agree with the statement.
2. Write a **D** if you disagree with the statement.

Before You Read	Cells—The Units of Life
	• Bacteria are the smallest organisms on Earth.
	• All living things are made up of one or more cells.
	• A cell's shape and size can be related to its function.
	• Cells are organized into systems to perform functions that keep an organism alive.

Construct the Foldable as directed at the beginning of this chapter.

Science Journal

Describe how building blocks fit together to build a larger structure.

Name ______________________________ Date ____________

Cells—The Units of Life

Section 1 The World of Cells

LE 1.1a: Living things are composed of cells. **1.1c** Most cells have cell membranes, genetic material, and cytoplasm. Some cells have a cell wall and/or chloroplasts. Many cells have a nucleus. **Also covered:** LE 1.1b

Skim *through Section 1 of your text. Write three questions that come to mind.*

1. ______________________________
2. ______________________________
3. ______________________________

Review Vocabulary

Use the term theory *in a sentence to illustrate its scientific meaning.*

theory ______________________________

New Vocabulary

Use the following key terms in a sentence to reflect their scientific meanings.

bacteria ______________________________

cell wall ______________________________

organelle ______________________________

photosynthesis ______________________________

Academic Vocabulary

Define convert *using a dictionary. Then use the word in a sentence to illustrate its scientific meaning.*

convert ______________________________

Name ______________________ Date ____________

Section 1 The World of Cells (continued)

Main Idea — **Details**

Importance of Cells

I found this information on page ________.

Summarize *the three main ideas of cell theory.*

	Cell Theory
1.	All living things are made up of one or more cells.
2.	
3.	

What are cells made of?

I found this information on page ________.

Organize *information you have learned about parts of a cell.*

Parts of a cell

I. The outside of the cell

A. ______________ (plants only)

supports and ______________

B. cell membrane

1. ______________

2. ______________

II. The inside of the cell

A. ______________

1. gelatin-like substance

2. ______________

B. ______________

1. ______________

a. stores ______________ in chromosomes

b. ______________

2. Vacuoles store ________, ________, ________, and ________

3. ______________ converts food energy into ______________

Main Idea	Details
What are cells made of? *I found this information on page* ______.	**Model** *an animal cell. Use your book to help you sketch an animal cell and label its parts.* cell membrane cytoplasm nucleus chromosomes mitochondrion vacuole
Energy and the Cell *I found this information on page* ______.	**Compare** *cellular respiration and* photosynthesis. *Label each input and output flow chart with these same five labels.* carbon dioxide food energy oxygen water

Cellular Respiration

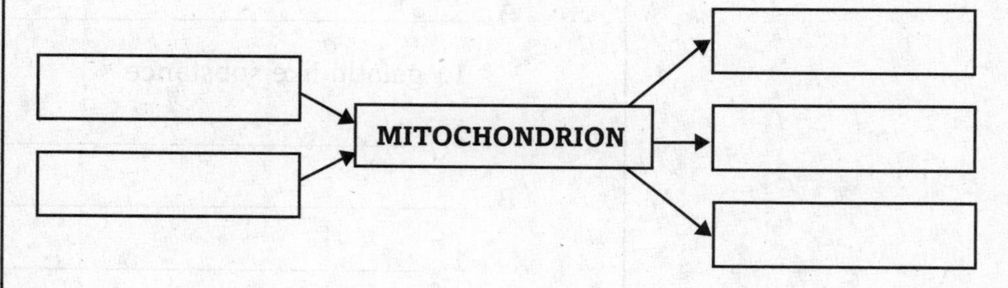

I found this information on page ______.

Photosynthesis

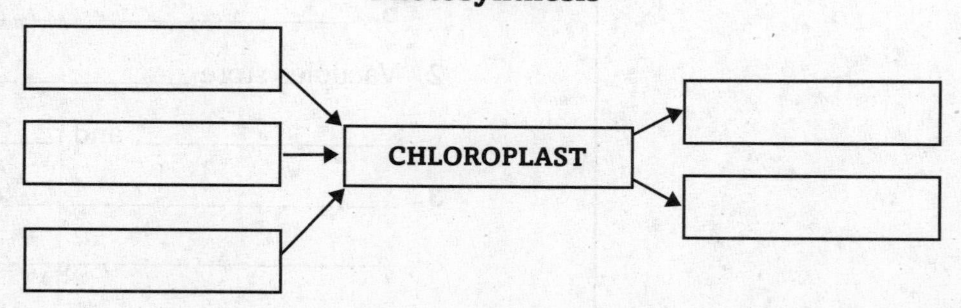

Name ______________________________ Date __________

Cells—The Units of Life

Section 2 The Different Jobs of Cells

LE 1.1e: Cells are organized for more effective functioning in multicellular organisms. Levels of organization for structure and function of a multicellular organism include cells, tissues, organs, and organ systems. **Also covered:** LE 1.1c, 1.1d, 1.1f, 1.1g

Skim *the section. Read the headings and the figure captions. Predict three topics that might be discussed in this section.*

1. ______________________________

2. ______________________________

3. ______________________________

Review Vocabulary

Define organism *using a dictionary.*

organism ______________________________

____

New Vocabulary

Read the definitions below. Write the key term on the blank in the left column.

__________ groups of similar cells that do the same type of work

__________ different types of tissues working together

__________ a group of organs that works together to do a certain job

Academic Vocabulary

Use a dictionary to define function. *Then use the term in a scientific sentence.*

function ______________________________

____

____

Name ______________________ Date ______________

Main Idea | **Details**

Special Cells for Special Jobs

I found this information on page ______.

Summarize *information from your book about human cells.*

Type of Cell	Description
Bone	
	long and have many branches to send and receive messages quickly
	usually long and have many fibers that can contract and relax
Skin	
Fat	

I found this information on page ______.

Identify *3 functions of plant cells.*

1. ______________
2. ______________
3. ______________

I found this information on page ______.

Compare and Contrast *human skin cells and the cells on the outside of a plant stem. Put the statements into the Venn diagram.*

- cells are flat and close together
- part of the outer layer of the organism
- cells are short and thick
- provide protection against sun and disease
- cells provide structure

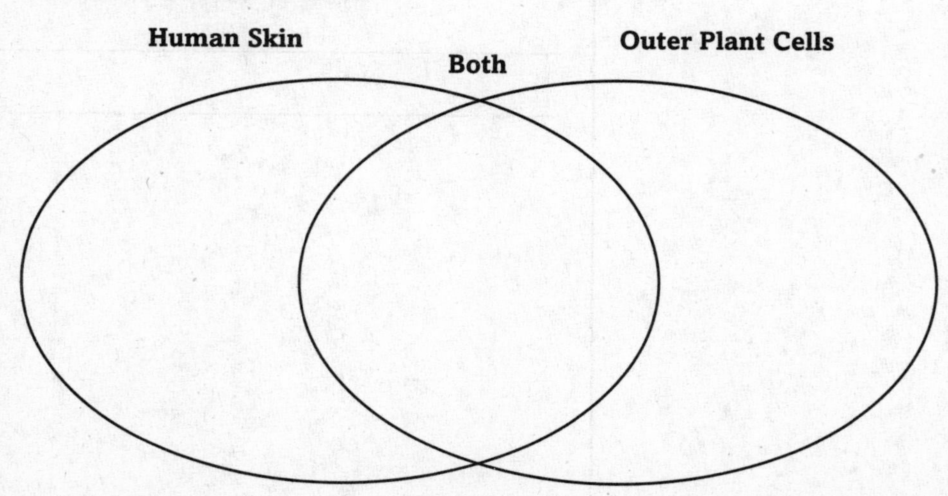

Name ______________________ Date ____________

Main Idea — **Details**

Cell Organization

I found this information on page ______.

Organize *information about cell organization by completing the outline.*

Cell organization of many-celled organisms

I. Tissues

A. Definition: ______

B. Example: ______

II. Organs

A. Definition: ______

B. Example: ______

Specific examples of tissue system

1. ______

2. ______

3. ______

III. Organ systems

A. Definition: ______

______

B. Example: ______

Specific examples of organs in system

1. ______

2. ______

3. ______

CONNECT IT Create an analogy between the jobs of nerve cells and fat cells to real-life careers. For example, skin cells help protect the body, and police officers help protect people.

______

______

______

Name ____________________________ Date __________

Cells—The Units of Life Chapter Wrap-Up

Now that you have read the chapter, think about what you have learned and complete the table below. Compare your previous answers with these.

1. Write an **A** if you agree with the statement.
2. Write a **D** if you disagree with the statement.

Cells—The Units of Life	After You Read
• Bacteria are the smallest organisms on Earth.	
• All living things are made up of one or more cells.	
• A cell's shape and size can be related to its function.	
• Cells are organized into systems to perform functions that keep an organism alive.	

Review

Use this checklist to help you study.

- ☐ Review the information you included in your Foldable.
- ☐ Study your *Science Notebook* on this chapter.
- ☐ Study the definitions of vocabulary words.
- ☐ Review daily homework assignments.
- ☐ Re-read the chapter and review the charts, graphs, and illustrations.
- ☐ Review the Self Check at the end of each section.
- ☐ Look over the Chapter Review at the end of the chapter.

SUMMARIZE IT **After reading this chapter, identify three things that you have learned about cells.**

____

____

____

____

Name ______________________________ Date ____________

Support, Movement, and Responses

Before You Read

Before you read the chapter, respond to these statements.

1. Write an **A** if you agree with the statement.
2. Write a **D** if you disagree with the statement.

Before You Read	Support, Movement, and Responses
	• Your skin is the largest organ of your body.
	• No matter how still you might be, some muscles in your body are always moving.
	• Living bone is an organ made of several different tissues.
	• The basic working units of the nervous system are nerve cells.

Construct the Foldable as directed at the beginning of this chapter.

Science Journal

Imagine for a moment that your body does not have a support system. How will you perform your daily activities? Explain your reasoning.

____

____

____

____

____

____

Name ______________________ Date ____________

Support, Movement, and Responses

Section 1 The Skin

LE 1.2a: Each system is composed of organs and tissues that perform specific functions and interact with each other.
1.2b: Tissues, organs, and organ systems help to provide all cells with nutrients, oxygen, and waste removal.
Also covered: LE 1.2g, 1.2h, 5.1a, 5.2f

Scan ***the section by following the checklist below.***

- ☐ Read all of the section headings.
- ☐ Read all of the bold words.
- ☐ Read all charts and graphs.
- ☐ Look at all of the pictures.
- ☐ Think about what you already know about the skin.

Write three facts that you discovered about the skin as you scanned this section.

1. ______________________
2. ______________________
3. ______________________

Review Vocabulary

Define organ ***as it relates to the body, and use it in an original sentence.***

organ ______________________

New Vocabulary

Use your book to define the following terms.

epidermis ______________________

melanin ______________________

Academic Vocabulary

Use a dictionary to define regulate.

regulate ______________________

Name ______________________________ Date ____________

Section 1 The Skin (continued)

Main Idea	Details
Skin Structures *I found this information on page ______.*	**Model** *the skin by drawing and labeling its parts.*
Skin Functions *I found this information on page ______.*	**Create** *a graphic organizer to identify the five major functions of the skin.*

Main Idea | **Details**

Skin Injuries and Repair

I found this information on page ________.

Complete *the graphic organizer to identify types of skin injuries.*

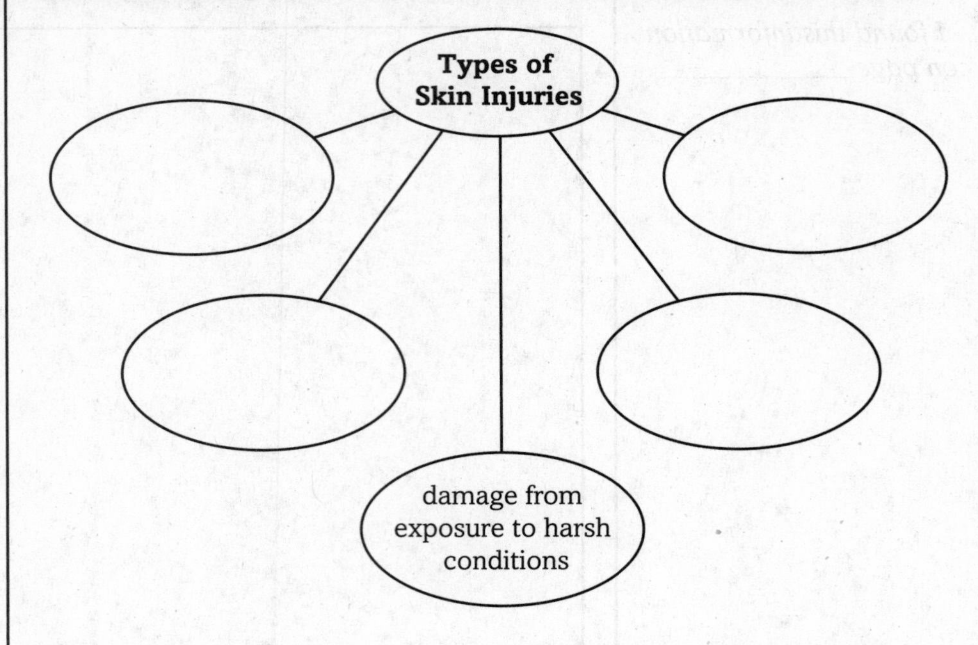

I found this information on page ________.

Sequence *the steps involved in the formation of a bruise and its healing.*

↓
Red blood cells leak into tissue and release hemoglobin.
↓
↓
↓

Name ______________________ Date ____________

Support, Movement, and Responses

Section 2 The Muscular System

LE 1.2a: Each system is composed of organs and tissues which perform specific functions and interact with each other. **1.2g:** Locomotion, necessary to escape danger, obtain food and shelter, and reproduce, is accomplished by the interaction of the skeletal and muscular systems, and coordinated by the nervous system.

Scan *the headings in Section 2. Read the headings and examine the illustrations. Write three questions that come to mind.*

1. ______________________
2. ______________________
3. ______________________

Review Vocabulary

Define muscle *using your book or a dictionary.*

muscle ______________________

New Vocabulary

Use your book to define the following terms. Then write a sentence for each term.

voluntary muscle ______________________

involuntary muscle ______________________

tendon ______________________

Academic Vocabulary

Use a dictionary to define voluntary.

voluntary ______________________

Name ______________________________ Date ____________

Main Idea | **Details**

Movement of the Human Body

I found this information on page ______.

Compare and contrast *movements of* voluntary *and* involuntary *muscles by using the terms provided to complete the Venn diagram.*

- able to relax
- controlled consciously
- able to contract
- cannot control consciously
- provides force for movement
- face muscle
- stomach muscle

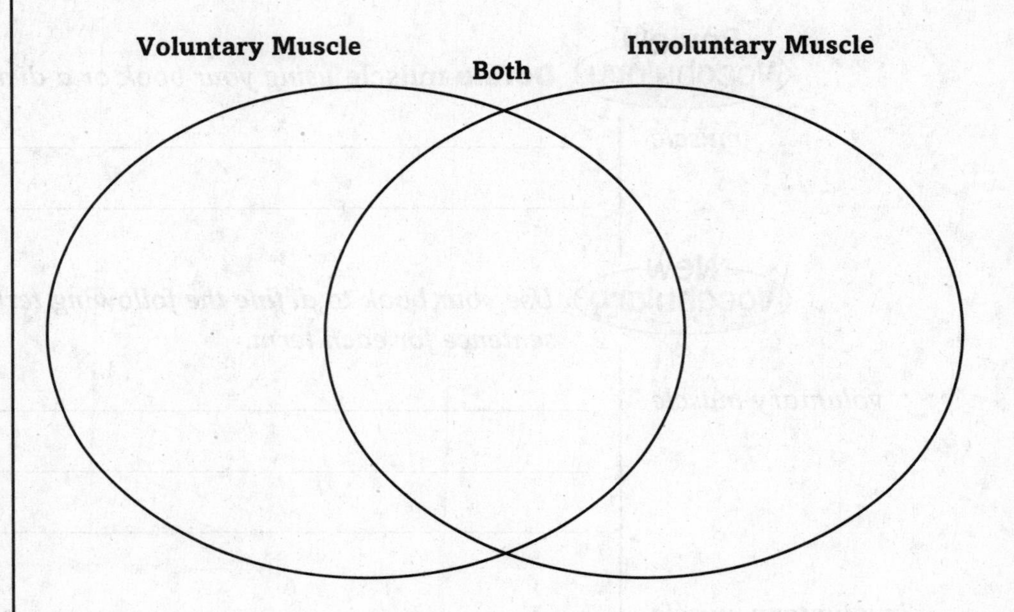

Classification of Muscle Tissue

I found this information on page ______.

Classify *the types of muscle tissues in the graphic organizer.*

Types of Muscle Tissues

Striated

Nonstriated

Main Idea | **Details**

Your Body's Simple Machines–Levers

I found this information on page ______.

Model *the three types of levers found in the body by providing simple drawings to illustrate the positions of the fulcrum, effort force, and load in each type.*

first-class lever	second-class lever	third-class lever

Working Muscles

I found this information on page ______.

Complete *the following paragraph about how muscles work by filling in the missing words or phrases.*

Muscles work together in ______________ so that your body can move. As one muscle ______________, the other ______________. Muscles ______________ push; they always ______________. When the muscles on the back of your upper leg contract, they ______________ and pull your lower leg back and up. When you straighten your leg, the muscles on the back of your upper leg ______________ and lengthen, and the muscles on the front of your upper leg ______________.

SYNTHESIZE IT Explain why a runner may have difficulty walking steadily after a long race.

____

____

____

____

Name ____________________ Date ____________

Support, Movement, and Responses

Section 3 The Skeletal System

LE 1.2a: Each system is composed of organs and tissues which perform specific functions and interact with each other. **1.2g:** Locomotion, necessary to escape danger, obtain food and shelter, and reproduce, is accomplished by the interaction of the skeletal and muscular systems, and coordinated by the nervous system.

Predict *three things that will be discussed in Section 3. Read the section's headings to help you make your predictions.*

1. ____________________
2. ____________________
3. ____________________

Review Vocabulary **Define** skeleton.

skeleton ____________________

New Vocabulary *Find a sentence in Section 3 that includes each vocabulary term.*

periosteum ____________________

cartilage ____________________

joint ____________________

ligament ____________________

Academic Vocabulary *Use a dictionary to define* internal.

internal ____________________

Name ______________________ Date ____________

Main Idea | **Details**

Functions of Your Skeletal System

I found this information on page ______.

Summarize *the functions of the* skeletal system *on the lines below.*

1. ______
2. ______
3. ______
4. ______
5. ______

Bone Structure

I found this information on page ______.

Distinguish compact bone *from* spongy bone *by identifying a characteristic and the importance of each type of bone.*

Type of Bone	Characteristic	Importance

I found this information on page ______.

Create *a graphic organizer to identify five characteristics of* cartilage *that make it important in joints.*

Main Idea	Details
Bone Formation *I found this information on page* ______.	**Compare** *the roles of* osteoblasts *and* osteoclasts *in the formation and breakdown of bone tissue.* Osteoblasts ______________________ ______________________ Osteoclasts ______________________ ______________________
Joints *I found this information on page* ______.	**Organize** *the different types of joints in a graphic organizer.*

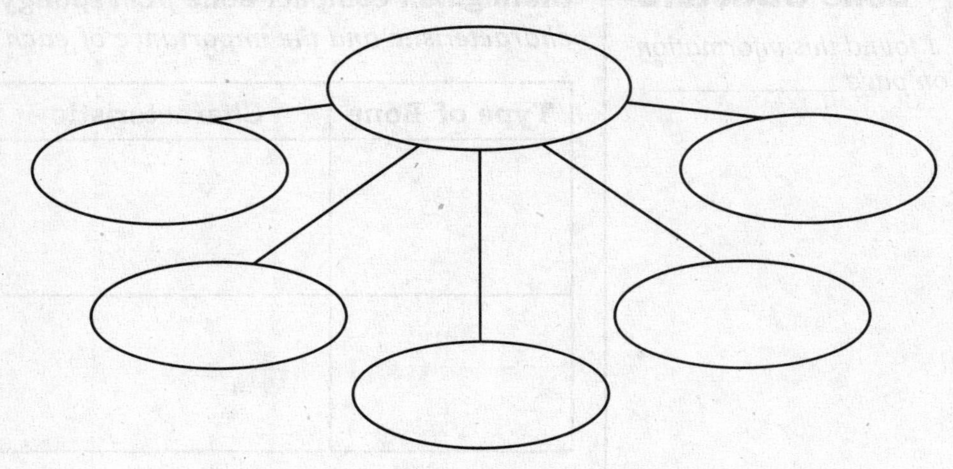

Main Idea	Details
I found this information on page ______.	**Summarize** *the* purpose of cartilage *at joints in the human body on the lines below.* ______________________ ______________________ ______________________ ______________________ ______________________

Name ________________________ Date ____________

Support, Movement, and Responses

Section 4 The Nervous System

LE 1.2h: The nervous and endocrine systems interact to control and coordinate the body's responses to changes in the environment, and to regulate growth, development, and reproduction. Hormones are chemicals produced by the endocrine system; hormones regulate many body functions. **Also covered:** LE 1.2a, 5.1a, 5.2f

Scan *the headings in Section 3 to identify the body's senses.*

1. ____________________
2. ____________________
3. ____________________
4. ____________________
5. ____________________

Review Vocabulary

Define homeostasis.

homeostasis ____________________

____

New Vocabulary

Scan *within the section for bold words and their meanings. Then write the correct term next to its definition.*

____________ brain and spinal cord

____________ all of the nerves that connect the brain and spinal cord to other body parts

____________ nerve cell

____________ small space in which an impulse crosses from one neuron to another

Academic Vocabulary

Use a dictionary to define adjust.

adjust ____________________

____

Name ______________________ Date ______________

Main Idea | **Details**

How the Nervous System Works

I found this information on page ______.

Complete *the graphic organizer below to illustrate how the* nervous system *acts as a control system for the body.*

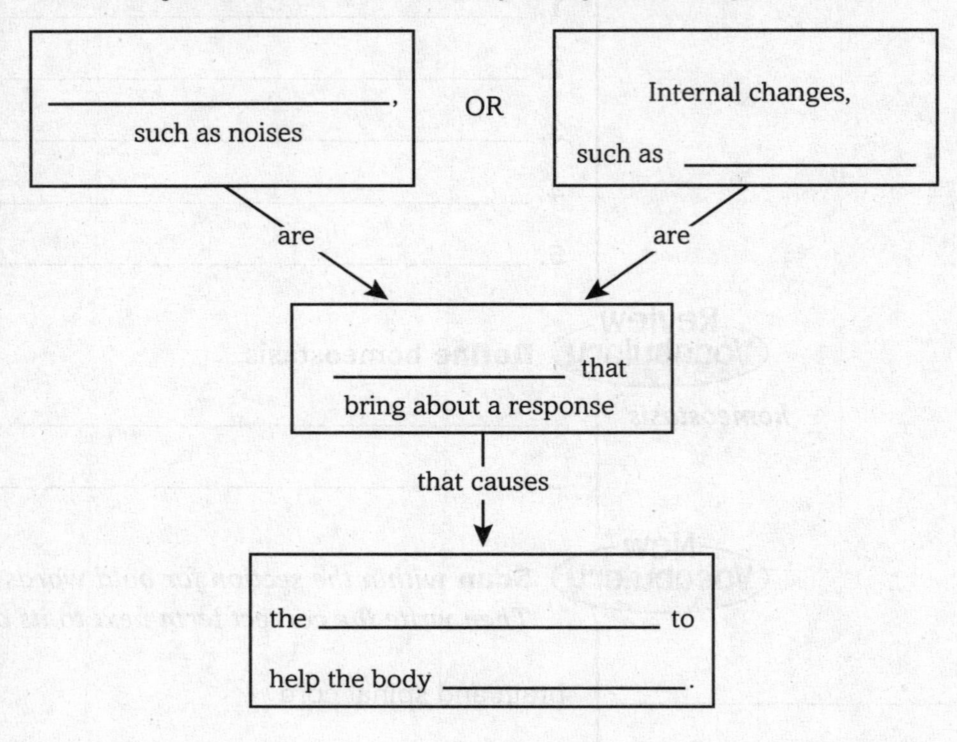

Nerve Cells

I found this information on page ______.

Sequence *the structures of a* neuron *in the order in which an impulse travels.*

1. ______ **2.** ______ **3.** ______

The Divisions of the Nervous System

I found this information on page ______.

Organize *the parts of the* nervous system *in this graphic organizer.*

Nervous System

Name ______________________ Date __________

Main Idea — Details

Safety and the Nervous System

I found this information on page ______.

Sequence *the reflex arc by tracing the path of* an impulse, *for example after a person touches a hot object.*

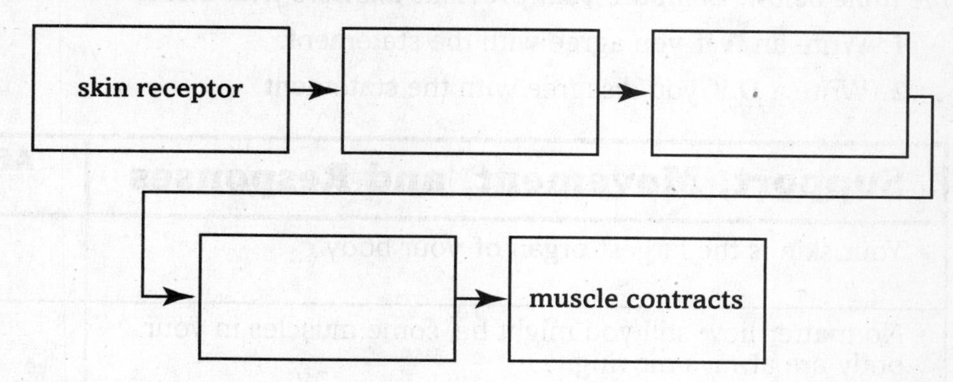

The Senses

I found this information on page ______.

Identify *the sensory organs and their* receptors *for each sense.*

Sense	Sensory Organ	Sensory Receptors
Smell		
Taste		
Vision		
Hearing		

Drugs Affect the Nervous System

I found this information on page ______.

Summarize *the effects of* depressants *and* stimulants *on the body.*

1. Depressants ______________________

____

2. Stimulants ______________________

____

CONNECT IT Evaluate how alcohol use could affect the ability of a person riding a bicycle.

____

____

____

Name ____________________ Date __________

Support, Movement, and Responses

Chapter Wrap-Up

Now that you have read the chapter, think about what you have learned and complete the table below. Compare your previous answers with these.

1. Write an **A** if you agree with the statement.
2. Write a **D** if you disagree with the statement.

Support, Movement, and Responses	After You Read
• Your skin is the largest organ of your body.	
• No matter how still you might be, some muscles in your body are always moving.	
• Living bone is an organ made of several different tissues.	
• The basic working units of the nervous system are nerve cells.	

Review

Use this checklist to help you study.

- ☐ Review the information you included in your Foldable.
- ☐ Study your *Science Notebook* on this chapter.
- ☐ Study the definitions of vocabulary words.
- ☐ Review daily homework assignments.
- ☐ Re-read the chapter and review the charts, graphs, and illustrations.
- ☐ Review the Self Check at the end of each section.
- ☐ Look over the Chapter Review at the end of the chapter.

SUMMARIZE IT **After reading this chapter, identify three main ideas that you have learned about body systems.**

____

____

____

Name ______________________________ Date __________

Circulation

Before You Read

Before you read the chapter, respond to these statements.

1. Write an **A** if you agree with the statement.
2. Write a **D** if you disagree with the statement.

Before You Read	Circulation
	• The human heart has four chambers.
	• Arteries are blood vessels that carry blood to the heart.
	• Platelets are cell fragments that help fight bacteria and viruses.
	• Lymphatic vessels are like veins in that they have valves.

Construct the Foldable as directed at the beginning of this chapter.

Science Journal

Infer how the circulatory system provides your body with the nutrients it needs to stay healthy.

___

___

___

___

___

___

Name ______________________ Date ______________

Circulation

Section 1 The Circulatory System

LE 1.2f: The circulatory system moves substances to and from cells, where they are needed or produced, responding to changing demands. **Also covered:** LE 1.2a, 1.2j

Scan *Section 1 of your book. Read the headings and look at the illustrations. Predict three things that will be discussed.*

1. ______________________
2. ______________________
3. ______________________

Review Vocabulary **Define** heart *using your book or a dictionary.*

heart ______________________

New Vocabulary *Read the definitions below. Write the correct vocabulary terms on the blanks in the left column.*

______ two upper chambers of the heart that contract at the same time

______ two lower chambers of the heart that contract at the same time

______ flow of blood to and from the tissues of the heart

______ flow of blood through the heart to the lungs and back to the heart

______ flow of blood from the heart to all of the organs and body tissues, except the heart and lungs, with oxygen-poor blood returning to the heart

______ blood vessel that carries blood away from the heart

______ blood vessel that carries blood back to the heart

______ microscopic blood vessel that connects arteries and veins

Academic Vocabulary *Use a dictionary to define* **transport** *as it would be used in science.*

transport ______________________

Name ______________________________ Date __________

Main Idea | **Details**

How Materials Move Through the Body

I found this information on page ________.

Compare and contrast diffusion *and* active transport *by completing the Venn diagram with at least five facts.*

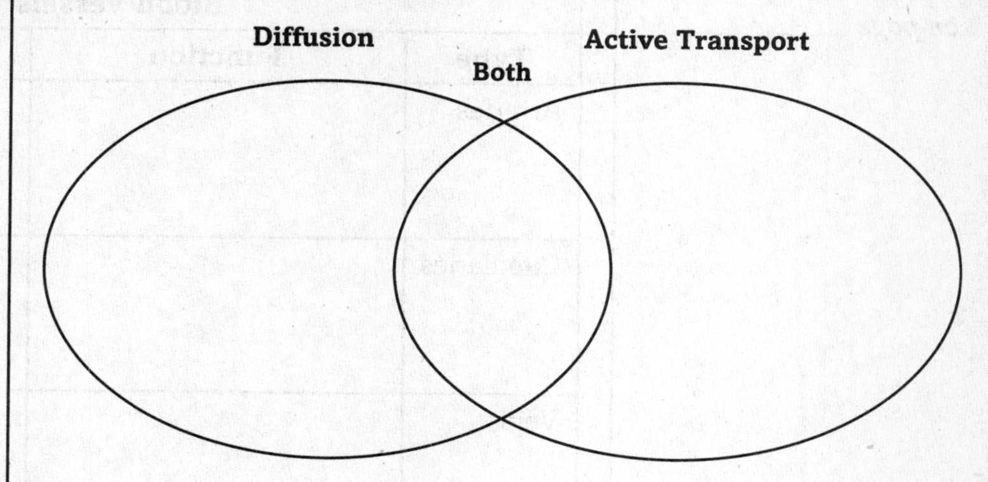

The Heart

I found this information on page ________.

Sequence *the stages in* pulmonary circulation *by completing the flow diagram. Include* aorta, pulmonary veins, pulmonary arteries, right atrium, left atrium, *and* right ventricle.

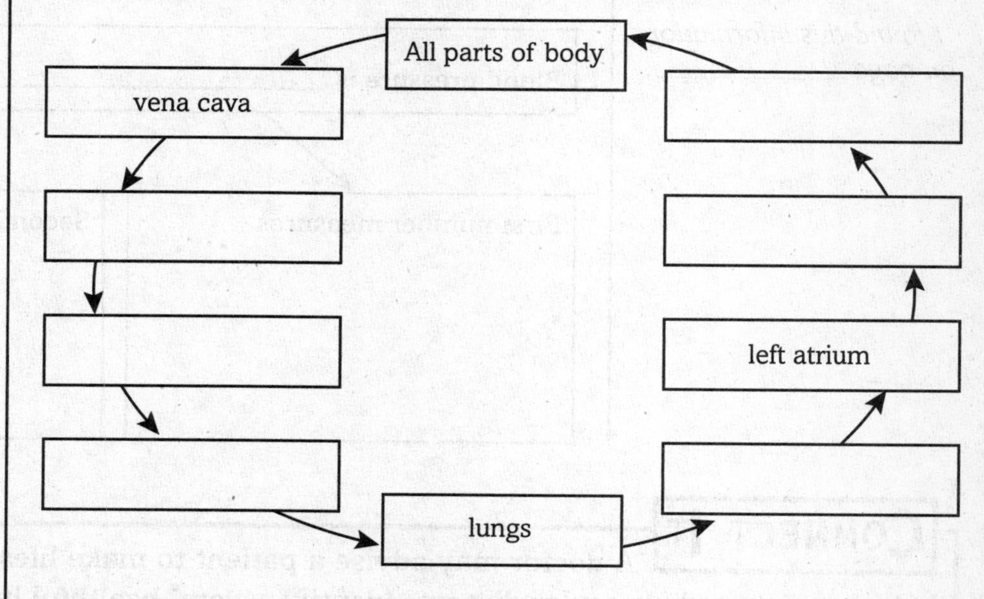

I found this information on page ________.

Summarize *the exchange that occurs between a* systemic capillary *and the* tissue cells *it serves.*

____

____

____

Main Idea — Details

Blood Vessels

I found this information on page ______.

Classify blood vessels *by completing the chart.*

Blood Vessels		
Type	**Function**	**Description**
Arteries		
Capillaries		
Veins		

Blood Pressure

I found this information on page ______.

Define blood pressure *and the two numbers used to measure it.*

Blood pressure is ______________________.

First number measures

Second number measures

CONNECT IT A doctor may advise a patient to make lifestyle changes to help prevent cardiovascular disease. Identify several healthful habits the doctor might suggest.

____

____

____

Name ____________________ Date ____________

Circulation

Section 2 Blood

LE 1.2f: The circulatory system moves substances to and from cells, where they are needed or produced, responding to changing demands. **Also covered:** LE 1.2a, 1.2 b, 1.2j

Skim *Section 2 of your book. Write three questions that come to mind. Look for answers to your questions as you read the section.*

1. ____________________

2. ____________________

3. ____________________

Review Vocabulary

Define blood vessels *using your book or a dictionary.*

blood vessels ____________________

New Vocabulary

Use your book or a dictionary to define the following terms.

platelet ____________________

plasma ____________________

hemoglobin ____________________

Academic Vocabulary

Use a dictionary to define series *as it would be used in science.*

series ____________________

Main Idea | **Details**

Functions of Blood

I found this information on page ________.

Create *a graphic organizer with facts about the* functions of blood.

Parts of Blood

I found this information on page ________.

Summarize *information about the* parts of blood *in the chart below.*

Parts of Blood	
Part	**Function**
Plasma	
Red blood cells	
White blood cells	
Platelets	

Blood Clotting

I found this information on page ________.

Sequence *the steps in* wound healing *by completing the blanks.*

________ stick to the wound and release ________ ________. Next, ________ forms a sticky net. The net traps ________ and ________ to form a clot. The ________ forms a ________. Then, ________ form under the ________. Finally, the ________ falls off.

Name ______________________________ Date ____________

Main Idea | **Details**

Blood Types

I found this information on page ______.

Compare and contrast *the 2 sets of* chemical identification tags in blood *by completing the Venn diagram with at least five facts.*

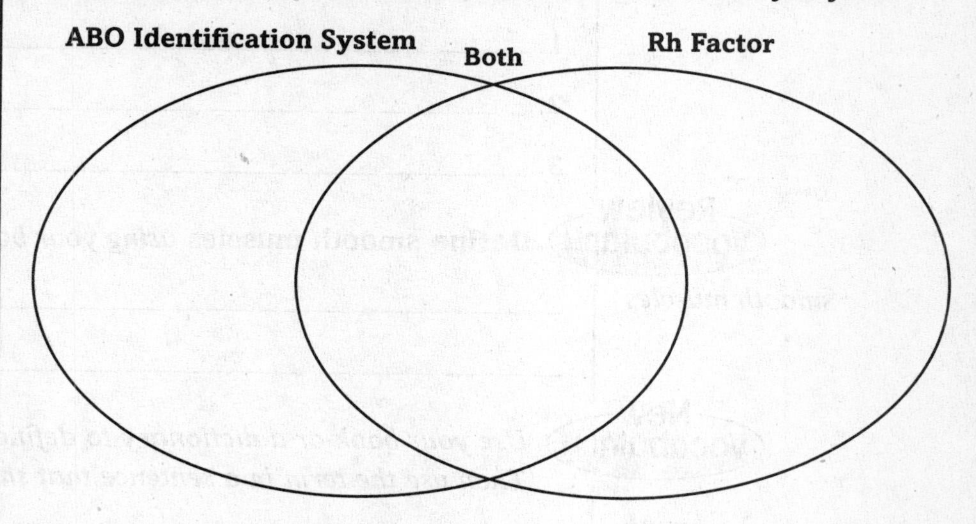

Diseases of Blood

I found this information on page ______.

Identify *causes and effects of* two diseases of the blood.

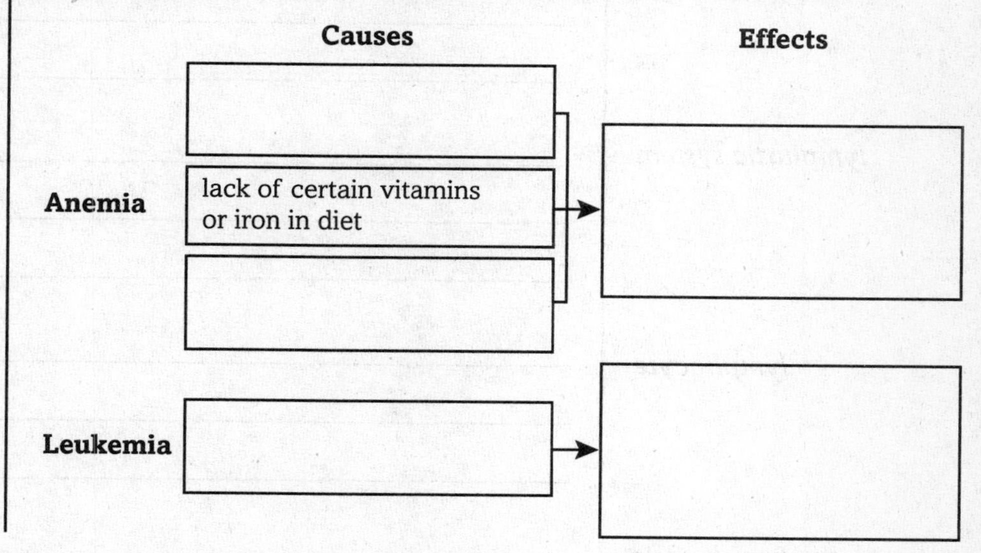

CONNECT IT Almost immediately after being born, a baby received a blood transfusion of Rh+ blood. Predict the mother's Rh factor. Why did the baby need a blood transfusion?

____

____

____

Name ______________________ Date ______________

Circulation

Section 3 The Lymphatic System

LE 1.2f: The circulatory system moves substances to and from cells, where they are needed or produced, responding to changing demands. **Also covered:** LE 1.2a, 1.2j

Scan *the* What You'll Learn *statements for Section 3 of your book. Identify three topics that will be discussed.*

1. ______________________
2. ______________________
3. ______________________

Review Vocabulary

Define smooth muscles *using your book or a dictionary.*

smooth muscles ______________________

New Vocabulary

Use your book or a dictionary to define each vocabulary term. Then use the term in a sentence that shows its scientific meaning.

lymph ______________________

lymphatic system ______________________

lymphocyte ______________________

lymph node ______________________

Academic Vocabulary

Use a dictionary to define occur *as it would be used in science.*

occur ______________________

Main Idea | **Details**

Functions of the Lymphatic System

I found this information on page ________.

Define tissue fluid *and describe its relationship to the* lymphatic system.

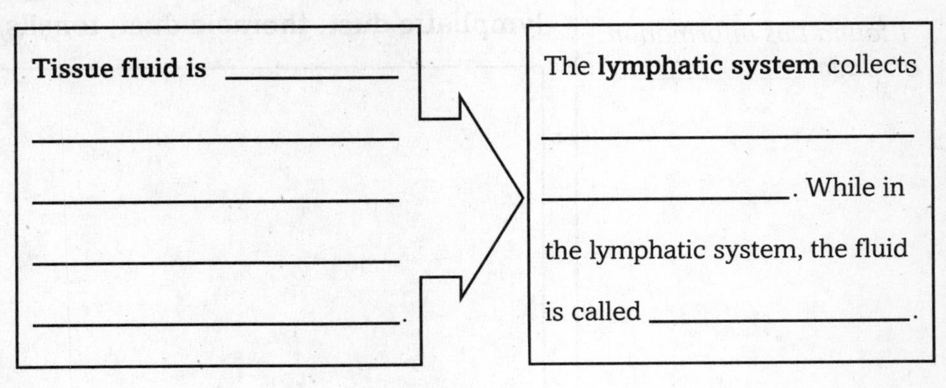

I found this information on page ________.

Sequence *the stages by which lymph travels through the lymphatic system.*

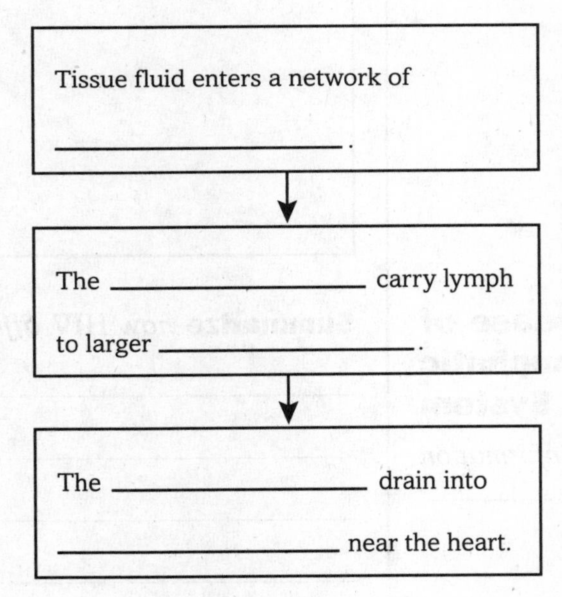

I found this information on page ________.

Summarize *how the* lymphatic system transports lymph. *Discuss the role of smooth muscles and valves.*

____

____

____

____

Name ______________________ Date ________

Main Idea | **Details**

Lymphatic Organs

I found this information on page _______.

Model *the* lymphatic system *by drawing it within an outline of the human body. Indicate and label* lymph nodes, lymph vessels, lymphatic duct, thoracic duct, tonsils, thymus, *and* spleen.

A Disease of the Lymphatic System

I found this information on page _______.

Summarize *how* HIV *affects the lymphatic system.*

____

____

____

____

CONNECT IT

Analyze why people who have HIV are at higher risk from the flu or pneumonia than people who are HIV-negative?

____

____

____

____

Name ______________________ Date __________

Tie It Together

A Checklist for Health

You know that a healthy lifestyle is important for the health of your cardiovascular system.

- Work with a partner to develop a checklist of daily actions to protect your cardiovascular health.
- List actions that are beneficial and actions that should be avoided.
- Provide concrete examples.
- Then make a poster using your checklist.

Name ______________________ Date __________

Circulation Chapter Wrap-Up

Now that you have read the chapter, think about what you have learned and complete the table below. Compare your previous answers with these.

1. Write an **A** if you agree with the statement.
2. Write a **D** if you disagree with the statement.

Circulation	After You Read
• The human heart has four chambers.	
• Arteries are blood vessels that carry blood to the heart.	
• Platelets are cell fragments that help fight bacteria and viruses.	
• Lymphatic vessels are like veins in that they have valves.	

Review

Use this checklist to help you study.

- [ ] Review the information you included in your Foldable.
- [ ] Study your *Science Notebook* on this chapter.
- [ ] Study the definitions of vocabulary words.
- [ ] Review daily homework assignments.
- [ ] Re-read the chapter and review the charts, graphs, and illustrations.
- [ ] Review the Self Check at the end of each section.
- [ ] Look over the Chapter Review at the end of the chapter.

SUMMARIZE IT

After reading this chapter, identify three main concepts that you have learned about circulation.

____

____

____

____

Name ______________________________ Date ____________

Digestion, Respiration, and Excretion

Before You Read

Preview the chapter title, the section titles, and the section headings. List at least one idea for each section in each column.

K What I know	W What I want to find out

FOLDABLES™ Study Organizer

Construct the Foldable as directed at the beginning of this chapter.

Science Journal

Write a paragraph describing what you do to help your body recover after an active game.

Name ______________________ Date ____________

Digestion, Respiration, and Excretion

Section 1 The Digestive System

LE 1.2c: The digestive system consists of organs that are responsible for the mechanical and chemical breakdown of food. The breakdown process results in molecules that can be absorbed and transported to cells. **Also covered:** LE 1.2a, 1.2b

Scan *the title and headings in Section 1. Predict three topics that might be discussed in this section.*

1. ______________________
2. ______________________
3. ______________________

Review Vocabulary *Write an original sentence to show the scientific meaning of the word* bacteria.

bacteria ______________________

New Vocabulary *Find a sentence in Section 1 that uses each vocabulary term or a form of the term.*

nutrient ______________________

enzyme ______________________

peristalsis ______________________

chyme ______________________

villi ______________________

Academic Vocabulary **Define** contract *as a verb using a dictionary.*

contract ______________________

Main Idea | **Details**

Functions of the Digestive System

I found this information on page ________.

Sequence *the steps of the digestive process. Identify what occurs during each step.*

Step: ______________

What happens: ______________

↓

Step: Digestion

What happens: ______________

Chemical: ______________

Mechanical: ______________

↓

Step: ______________

What happens: ______________

↓

Step: ______________

What happens: ______________

Enzymes

I found this information on page ________.

Summarize *how* enzymes *are important by completing the statements below.*

Enzymes ______________ and help you digest ______________.

They are produced in ______________ ______________.

Enzymes also are important because they ______________ ______________ and ______________.

Name ______________________________ Date ______________

Main Idea | **Details**

Organs of the Digestive System

I found this information on page ______________.

Model and label *the organs involved in digestion. Circle the labels of organs that are part of the digestive tract.*

Bacteria Are Important

I found this information on page ______________.

Identify *two ways bacteria in the digestive system help the body.*

1. ____

____

2. ____

____

SUMMARIZE IT

Suppose you eat a sandwich that provides protein, carbohydrates, and fat. Describe what happens to the sandwich as it moves through your digestive system.

____

____

____

____

Name ________________________________ Date __________

Digestion, Respiration, and Excretion

Section 2 Nutrition

LE 5.2b: Foods contain a variety of substances. Each substance is vital to the survival of the organism. **5.2e:** In order to maintain a balanced state, all organisms have a minimum daily intake of each type of nutrient. An imbalance in any of the nutrients might result in weight gain, weight loss, or a diseased state. **Also covered:** LE 5.2a, 5.2d

Scan *the illustrations in Section 2. Write three questions that come to mind. As you read, look for answers to your questions.*

1. ________________________________

2. ________________________________

3. ________________________________

Review Vocabulary

Define molecule *to show its scientific meaning.*

molecule ________________________________

____

New Vocabulary

Use your book to define the following terms.

amino acid ________________________________

____

carbohydrate ________________________________

____

vitamin ________________________________

____

mineral ________________________________

____

Academic Vocabulary

Use a dictionary to define source. *Then write an original sentence using the term.*

source ________________________________

____

____

Name ______________________________ Date ______________

Main Idea | **Details**

Why do you eat?

I found this information on page ________.

Complete *the paragraph to summarize the importance of food.*

Food provides ______________________________________.
The ______________________ of food is its most important quality,
but many people choose food based on ______________________
and ______________________.

Classes of Nutrients

I found this information on page ________.

Identify *the 6 major classes of nutrients.*

1. ______________ 3. ______________ 5. ______________
2. ______________ 4. ______________ 6. ______________

Summarize *why proteins are important nutrients.*

____

____

I found this information on page ________.

Organize *information about the three types of* carbohydrates.

Type	Food Sources	Use in Body
Sugar		
Starch		
Fiber		

I found this information on page ________.

Summarize *four functions that fat has in the body.*

1. ____
2. ____
3. ____
4. ____

Name ______________________ Date __________

Section 2 Nutrition (continued)

Main Idea — Details

I found this information on page ______.

Distinguish *between water-soluble and fat-soluble* vitamins.

Water-Soluble Vitamins	Fat-Soluble Vitamins

I found this information on page ______.

Label *each description with the mineral it describes.*

______ helps clot blood and maintain strong teeth and bones.

______ helps muscle contraction.

______ allows oxygen to be transported by red blood cells.

Food Groups

I found this information on page ______.

Model *serving size for different food categories.*

Group	Recommended Servings per Day	Examples of 1 Serving Size
Bread and cereal		
Fruits		
Vegetables		
Milk, yogurt, or cheese		
Meat, beans, and eggs		

CONNECT IT Plan a daily menu that provides the recommended servings from each food group. Identify some nutrients that each food in your menu provides.

____

____

____

Name ______________________ Date __________

Digestion, Respiration, and Excretion

Section 3 The Respiratory System

LE 1.2d: During respiration, cells use oxygen to release the energy stored in food. The respiratory system supplies oxygen and removes carbon dioxide (gas exchange).
Also covered: LE 1.2a, 1.2j

Scan *Section 3 using the checklist below.*

- ☐ Read all headings.
- ☐ Read all bold words.
- ☐ Look at each illustration.
- ☐ Think about what you already know about breathing.

Write two predictions you have for subjects that will be covered in this section.

1. ______________________

2. ______________________

Review Vocabulary

Define diaphragm *as it relates to the respiratory system.*

diaphragm ______________________

New Vocabulary

Write the vocabulary term that matches each definition.

__________ tiny, thin-walled sacs at the end of bronchioles

__________ air-conducting tube that connects the larynx with the bronchi

__________ airway to which the vocal cords are attached

__________ two short tubes that carry air into the lungs

Academic Vocabulary

Read the sentence below. Analyze what* coordinate *means in this sentence.

Your brain coordinates the movement of the muscles in your throat, tongue, cheeks, and lips when you talk.

coordinate ______________________

Main Idea	Details
Functions of the Respiratory System *I found this information on page* ______.	**Sequence** *the process of breathing and cellular respiration.* Breathing in brings oxygen into the body. ↓ Blood ______. ↓ Cells ______. ↓ Cells produce carbon dioxide and water as waste. ↓ Blood ______. ↓ Breathing out ______.
Organs of the Respiratory System *I found this information on page* ______.	**Create** *a drawing of the respiratory system. Label the* nasal cavity, larynx, pharynx, trachea, lungs, bronchi, *and* alveoli. *Write a caption explaining the function of each part of the system.*

Name ______________________________ Date ____________

Main Idea | **Details**

Why do you breathe?

I found this information on page ______.

Analyze *how carbon dioxide in the blood affects breathing rate.*

____

____

Model *the role of the diaphragm in breathing. Make one diagram of the lungs and diaphragm for when a person inhales and one for exhaling. Use arrows to show how the lungs and diaphragm move.*

Diseases and Disorders of the Respiratory System

I found this information on page ______.

Classify *respiratory diseases and disorders. Complete the chart.*

Disease or Disorder	Cause or Contributing Factors
Respiratory infections	
Chronic bronchitis	
Lung cancer	
Asthma	

SYNTHESIZE IT **Describe how emphysema affects cellular respiration and cell function.**

____

____

____

Name ______________________ Date ____________

Digestion, Respiration, and Excretion

Section 4 The Excretory System

LE 1.2e: The excretory system functions in the disposal of dissolved waste molecules, the elimination of liquid and gaseous wastes, and the removal of excess heat energy. **Also covered:** 1.2a

Read *the* What You'll Learn *statements for Section 4. Rewrite each statement as a question. As you read, look for the answers to your questions.*

1. ______________________________

____

2. ______________________________

____

3. ______________________________

____

Review Vocabulary

Define capillary *to show its scientific meaning.*

capillary ______________________________

____

New Vocabulary

Use your book to define the following terms.

nephron ______________________________

____

ureter ______________________________

____

bladder ______________________________

____

Academic Vocabulary

Use a dictionary to define eliminate. *Then rewrite the following sentence, substituting the meaning you found for the word* eliminate.

You eliminate some salts when you sweat.

eliminate ______________________________

____

Name ______________________________ Date ______________

Main Idea | **Details**

Functions of the Excretory System

I found this information on page ________.

Summarize *the ways in which the body excretes, or removes, waste. Complete the chart to show what each body system excretes.*

Excretion	
Digestive System	Respiratory System
Skin	Urinary System

Analyze *the importance of excretion by completing the sentence.*

If the body did not excrete wastes, ______________________________

____

The Urinary System

I found this information on page ________.

Summarize *the function of each part of the urinary system.*

Kidneys: ______________________________

Renal arteries: ______________________________

Renal veins: ______________________________

Ureters: ______________________________

Bladder: ______________________________

Urethra: ______________________________

Name ____________________ Date __________

Main Idea | **Details**

I found this information on page ______.

Sequence *the steps of filtration in the kidneys.*

1.	Blood enters the kidneys through the renal artery.
2.	
3.	
4.	
5.	
6.	The liquid left behind flows into collecting tubules and then into ureters.

Urinary Diseases and Disorders

I found this information on page ______.

Identify *the effects of kidney failure.*

____

____

____

____

SYNTHESIZE IT Identify effects of excretory system malfunction.

____

____

____

____

____

Name ______________________________ Date __________

Digestion, Respiration, and Excretion

Chapter Wrap-Up

Review the ideas you listed in the chart at the beginning of the chapter. Cross out any incorrect information in the first column. Then complete the chart by filling in the third column. How do your ideas compare with those you provided at the beginning of the chapter?

K What I know	W What I want to find out	L What I learned

Review

Use this checklist to help you study.

- ☐ Review the information you included in your Foldable.
- ☐ Study your *Science Notebook* on this chapter.
- ☐ Study the definitions of vocabulary words.
- ☐ Review daily homework assignments.
- ☐ Re-read the chapter and review the charts, graphs, and illustrations.
- ☐ Review the Self Check at the end of each section.
- ☐ Look over the Chapter Review at the end of the chapter.

SUMMARIZE IT **Identify the three most important ideas from this chapter.**

____

____

____

____

Name ______________________ Date ____________

Invertebrate Animals

Before You Read

Before you read the chapter, respond to these statements.

1. Write an **A** if you agree with the statement.
2. Write a **D** if you disagree with the statement.

Before You Read	Invertebrate Animals
	• Most animals have a backbone.
	• Animals are made up of many cells and have many different types of cells.
	• Animals can make their own food.
	• All animals can digest their food.
	• All animals can move from place to place.

Construct the Foldable as directed at the beginning of this chapter.

Science Journal

Describe similarities and differences between you and an aquatic invertebrate animal such as a nudibranch, which is a type of sea slug.

Name ______________________ Date ____________

Invertebrate Animals

Section 1 What is an animal?

LE 1.1h: Living things are classified by shared characteristics on the cellular and organism level. In classifying organisms, biologists consider details of internal and external structures.
Also covered: LE 1.1e, 1.1g, 1.2c, 1.2g, 5.1a, 5.1c, 5.1d, 5.1e, 5.1f, 5.1g

Preview *Section 1 by reading the headings. Write three questions you have about the content of the section.*

1. ______________________
2. ______________________
3. ______________________

Review Vocabulary

Define organelle *using your book or a dictionary.*

organelle ______________________

New Vocabulary

Define the following key terms. Below each definition, copy one sentence from Section 1 of your book that uses the word. Do not copy the sentence that gives the definition.

symmetry ______________________

invertebrate ______________________

Academic Vocabulary

Use a dictionary to define indicate.

indicate ______________________

Name ______________________________ Date ______________

Main Idea | **Details**

Animal Characteristics

I found this information on page ______________.

Complete *the following chart by writing a statement about each characteristic of animals.*

Animals	
Characteristic	Statement
Cells	
Nucleus and organelles	
Obtaining energy	
Digesting food	
Movement	

Symmetry

I found this information on page ______________.

Compare *forms of animal* symmetry *by drawing an example for each of the three types of symmetry below.*

Asymmetry	Bilateral Symmetry	Radial Symmetry

Name ______________________________ Date ____________

Main Idea — **Details**

Animal Classification

I found this information on page ________.

Classify *the types of* invertebrates *in the chart below.*

Animal Kingdom			
Invertebrates			

CONNECT IT Design an imaginary animal species. Keep in mind the five common characteristics of animals. Give your animal species a name. Draw it and label its parts.

My animal species: ______________________________

Name ______________________ Date ____________

Invertebrate Animals

Section 2 Sponges, Cnidarians, Flatworms, and Roundworms

LE 5.1b: An organism's overall body plan and its environment determine the way that the organism carries out the life processes. **Also covered:** LE 1.1h, 4.a, 5.1a, 5.1d, 5.1e

Scan *the figures in Section 2 of your book. Write three questions that come to your mind.*

1. ______________________

2. ______________________

3. ______________________

Review Vocabulary

Define species *to show its scientific meaning.*

species ______________________

New Vocabulary

Use your book to define the following key terms.

cnidarian ______________________

polyp ______________________

medusa ______________________

Academic Vocabulary

Use your book or a dictionary to find two meanings for the term segment. *Write both definitions below.*

segment ______________________

Main Idea | **Details**

Sponges

I found this information on page ________.

Organize *the information about sponges by filling in the key information.*

A. Filter feeders

____

____

B. Body support and defense

____

____

C. Sponge reproduction

____

____

Cnidarians

I found this information on page ________.

Compare *the two body forms of* cnidarians *by describing them in words and by drawing them in the chart below.*

Cnidarian Body Forms		
Form	**Description**	**Drawing**
Polyp		
Medusa		

Name ______________________ Date ____________

Section 2 Sponges, Cnidarians, Flatworms, and Roundworms (continued)

Main Idea — **Details**

Cnidarian Reproduction

I found this information on page ______.

Sequence *the main stages of reproduction in* medusa *forms of cnidarian, starting and ending with larva. Refer to the life cycle diagram in your book if you need help.*

1. ______________________
2. ______________________
3. ______________________
4. ______________________
5. ______________________

Flatworms And Roundworms

I found this information on page ______.

Compare and contrast *characteristics of flatworms and roundworms by completing the chart below.*

	Flatworms	Roundworms
Body shape		
Body openings		
Body construction		
Digestive system		

CONNECT IT Evaluate how the ability to move from place to place would give an invertebrate an advantage in getting food and reproducing.

____

____

____

Name ______ Date ______

Invertebrate Animals

Section 3 Mollusks and Segmented Worms

LE 5.1a: Animals and plants have a great variety of body plans and internal structures that contribute to their ability to maintain a balanced condition. **Also covered:** LE 5.1b, 5.1d, 5.1g

Scan *Section 3 of your textbook. Then write two facts that you learned about mollusks and segmented worms.*

1. ______

2. ______

Review Vocabulary **Define** organ *using your book as it applies to living organisms.*

organ ______

New Vocabulary *Define the following key terms.*

mollusk ______

mantle ______

radula ______

open circulatory system ______

closed circulatory system ______

Academic Vocabulary *Use a dictionary to define the word* rigid.

rigid ______

Main Idea | **Details**

Mollusks

I found this information on page ________.

Organize *the information in your book by writing the six important characteristics of* mollusks.

1. ______________________________
2. ______________________________
3. ______________________________
4. ______________________________
5. ______________________________
6. ______________________________

Types of Mollusks

I found this information on page ________.

Classify *the three types of mollusks by completing the chart below.*

Mollusks			
Types			
Where do they live?			
How many shells?			
Examples			

Cephalapods

I found this information on page ________.

Describe *the movement of a squid in water. Refer to the drawing of a balloon in your book if you need help.*

____

____

____

____

____

Name ______________________________ Date ____________

Section 3 Mollusks and Segmented Worms (continued)

Main Idea | **Details**

Segmented Worms

I found this information on page ________.

Summarize *the four characteristics of segmented worms below.*

1. ______________________________
2. ______________________________
3. ______________________________
4. ______________________________

Types of Segmented Worms

I found this information on page ________.

Classify *types of segmented worms by completing the chart.*

Types of Segmented Worms			
Type	**Where Found**	**Source of Energy**	**An Interesting Characteristic**
Earthworm			
Leech			
Marine worm			

CONNECT IT Write an account of an hour in the life of an earthworm. Include information about how the worm moves and eats.

____

____

____

Name ______________________________ Date ____________

Invertebrate Animals

Section 4 Arthropods and Echinoderms

LE 4.3d: Patterns of development vary among animals. **5.1a:** Animals and plants have a great variety of body plans and internal structures that contribute to their ability to maintain a balanced condition. **Also covered:** LE 5.1b, 5.1d, 5.1g

Scan *the illustrations in this section. Write four things you learned about arthropods and echinoderms from the illustrations.*

1. ______________________________
2. ______________________________
3. ______________________________
4. ______________________________

Review Vocabulary

Define regeneration *using your book or a dictionary.*

regeneration ______________________________

New Vocabulary

Define the following vocabulary terms.

arthropod ______________________________

appendage ______________________________

exoskeleton ______________________________

metamorphosis ______________________________

Academic Vocabulary

Use your book or a dictionary to define inject. *Use the word in a sentence about how spiders capture prey.*

inject ______________________________

Name ______________________ Date ______________

Main Idea | Details

Arthropods

I found this information on page ________.

Organize *information from your book by filling in the web diagram with the five characteristics shared by all* **arthropods.**

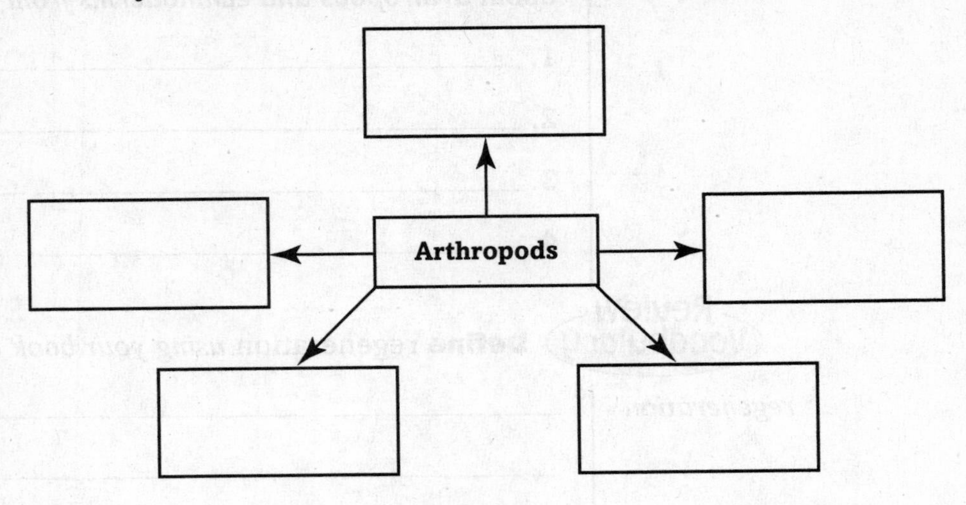

I found this information on page ________.

Analyze *the information in your book to complete the following chart about the four types of arthropods.*

Types of Arthropods	
Type	**Characteristics**
Insects	
Arachnids	
Centipedes and millipedes	
Crustaceans	

Name ______________________ Date ____________

Main Idea | **Details**

I found this information on page ______.

Sequence *the stages of complete and incomplete* metamorphosis *by labeling the charts.*

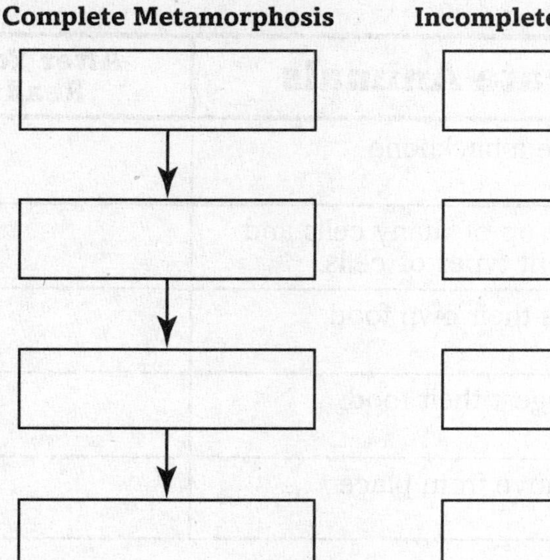

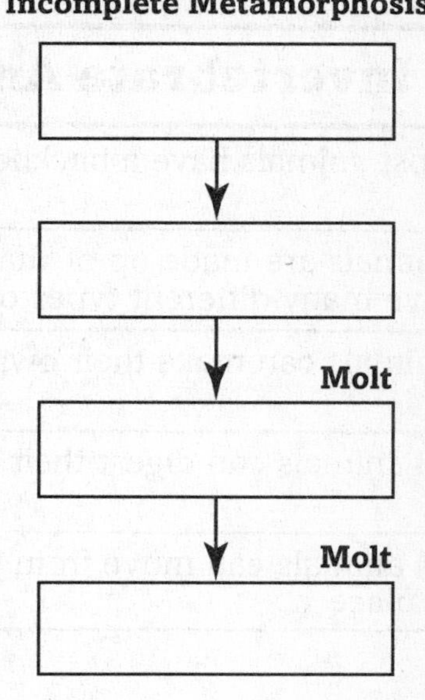

Echinoderms

I found this information on page ______.

Summarize *characteristics common to echinoderms by making a list of characteristics below.*

1. ______________________
2. ______________________
3. ______________________
4. ______________________

CONNECT IT Compare the circulatory systems of an insect and an earthworm.

____

____

____

____

____

Name ______________________________ Date ______________

Invertebrate Animals Chapter Wrap-Up

Now that you have read the chapter, think about what you have learned and complete the table below. Compare your previous answers with these.

1. Write an **A** if you agree with the statement.
2. Write a **D** if you disagree with the statement.

Invertebrate Animals	After You Read
• Most animals have a backbone.	
• Animals are made up of many cells and have many different types of cells.	
• Animals can make their own food.	
• All animals can digest their food.	
• All animals can move from place to place.	

Review

Use this checklist to help you study.

- ☐ Review the information you included in your Foldable.
- ☐ Study your *Science Notebook* on this chapter.
- ☐ Study the definitions of vocabulary words.
- ☐ Review daily homework assignments.
- ☐ Re-read the chapter and review the charts, graphs, and illustrations.
- ☐ Review the Self Check at the end of each section.
- ☐ Look over the Chapter Review at the end of the chapter.

SUMMARIZE IT

After reading this chapter, identify three things that you have learned about invertebrate animals.

____

____

____

____

Name ____________________ Date ________

Vertebrate Animals

Before You Read

Before you read the chapter, think about what you know about the topic. List three things that you already know about animals with backbones in the first column. Then list three things that you would like to learn about them in the second column.

K What I know	W What I want to find out

Construct the Foldable as directed at the beginning of this chapter.

Science Journal

An eagle, a salmon, a snake, and a grizzly bear all have a backbone. List other traits these animals and humans share.

Name ______________________________ Date ____________

Vertebrate Animals

Section 1 Chordate Animals

LE 5.1a: Animals and plants have a great variety of body plans and internal structures that contribute to their ability to maintain a balanced condition. **Also covered:** LE 1.1h, 5.1b, 5.1d, 5.1e, 5.1f, 5.1g

Skim *the headings in Section 3. Then make three predictions about what you will learn.*

1. ______________________________
2. ______________________________
3. ______________________________

Define *Write the correct word next to each definition.*

______________ an animal without a backbone

______________ an animal with a notochord, a nerve cord, and pharyngeal pouches sometime during development

______________ a vertebrate whose body temperature changes as the surrounding temperature changes

______________ an animal whose body temperature does not change with changes in the surrounding temperature

______________ a tough flexible tissue that is similar to bone but not as hard or brittle

Use a dictionary to define maintain.

maintain ______________________________

____

Name ______________________ Date ______________

Main Idea | **Details**

What is a chordate?

I found this information on page ______.

Identify *and describe three characteristics of all chordates that appear at some time during their development.*

Chordates		
Characteristic		Description
1.		
2.		
3.		

I found this information on page ______.

Model *a simple chordate by copying the sketch of the lancelet. Sketch a human next to it.*

Name each human structure with the same function as the following lancelet structures.

- notochord: ______________________
- nerve cord: ______________________
- gill slit: ______________________

I found this information on page ______.

Compare *the characteristics that all chordates share to the characteristics that only vertebrates share.*

All Chordates	Only Vertebrates

Name ________________ Date ________

Main Idea | **Details**

Fish and Types of Fish

I found this information on page ______.

Contrast *the characteristics of bony fish, jawless fish, and cartilaginous fish by completing the diagram. Write 3–4 characteristics for each type.*

Characteristics of All Fish		
Bony Fish	Jawless Fish	Cartilaginous Fish

I found this information on page ______.

Analyze *the adaptations of a typical bony fish. Use the figure in your book to help you sketch and label the fish.*

CONNECT IT Compare ectotherms and endotherms. Hypothesize about the advantages and disadvantages of each.

Name ______________________ Date __________

Vertebrate Animals

Section 2 Amphibians and Reptiles

LE 4.3d: Patterns of development vary among animals. In some species the young resemble the adult, while in others they do not. Some insects and amphibians undergo metamorphosis as they mature. **Also covered:** LE 4.3f, 5.1a, 5.1b

Scan *Section 1 of your book. Then write three questions that you have about amphibians and reptiles. Try to answer your questions as you read.*

1. ______________________
2. ______________________
3. ______________________

Review Vocabulary **Define** metamorphosis *to show its scientific meaning.*

metamorphosis ______________________

____

New Vocabulary *Use a dictionary or your book to define each key term.*

hibernation ______________________

____

estivation ______________________

____

amniotic egg ______________________

____

Academic Vocabulary *Use a dictionary to define* internal.

internal ______________________

____

Name ____________________ Date __________

Main Idea | **Details**

Amphibians

I found this information on page ________.

Complete *the prompts about amphibians.*

Definition: ____________________

____

Origin of the word *amphibian:* ____________________

____

Examples: ____________________

____

I found this information on page ________.

Contrast *hibernation and estivation in amphibians by completing the Venn diagram with at least five facts.*

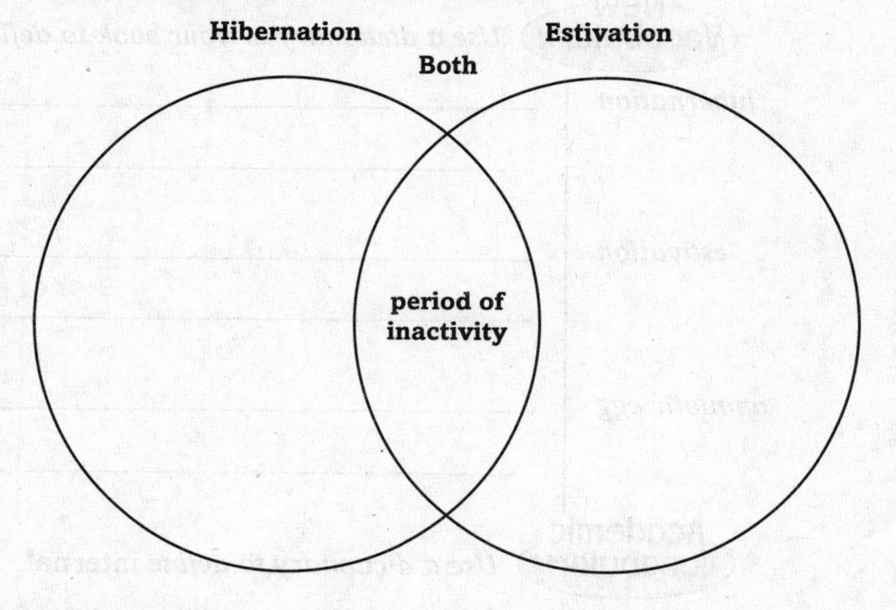

I found this information on page ________.

Organize *amphibian characteristics by listing them below.*

1. ____________________
2. ____________________
3. ____________________
4. ____________________
5. ____________________

Name ____________________ Date __________

Main Idea — Details

Reptiles

I found this information on page ________.

Organize *information about reptiles by completing the diagram.*

Turtles	Crocodiles and Alligators
Lizards	**Snakes**

I found this information on page ________.

Summarize *adaptations that are typical of reptiles by completing the chart.*

Reptile Adaptations	
Characteristic	**Purpose**
Skin	
Neck	
Lungs	
Internal fertilization	
Amniotic eggs	

CONNECT IT

Compare and contrast amphibians and reptiles.

____

____

____

____

Name ______________________________ Date ____________

Vertebrate Animals

Section 3 Birds

LE 5.1b: An organism's overall body plan and its environment determine the way that the organism carries out the life processes. **Also covered:** LE 5.1a, 5.1d, 5.1e

Skim *the headings in Section 3. Then make 3 predictions about what you will learn.*

1. ______________________________
2. ______________________________
3. ______________________________

Review Vocabulary

Define appendage *to show its scientific meaning. Think of two examples of appendages.*

appendage ______________________________

____

New Vocabulary

Use your book to define and sketch each type of feather.

contour feather ______________________________

____

____

down feather ______________________________

____

____

Academic Vocabulary

Use a dictionary to define constant.

constant ______________________________

____

Name ______________________________ Date ____________

Main Idea | **Details**

Characteristics of Birds

I found this information on page ______.

List *six characteristics of birds.*

1. ______________________________
2. ______________________________
3. ______________________________
4. ______________________________
5. ______________________________
6. ______________________________

Adaptations for Flight

I found this information on page ______.

Analyze *how birds are adapted for flight. Make a concept web that includes five adaptations.*

Main Idea | **Details**

Functions of Feathers

I found this information on page ______.

Compare and contrast *contour feathers and down feathers. List characteristics of each type of feather.*

Down Feathers	Contour Feathers
1.	1.
2.	2.
3.	3.
4.	4.

I found this information on page ______.

Analyze *at least three reasons why birds preen.*

1. ______________________________

2. ______________________________

3. ______________________________

COMPARE IT Analyze which would be warmer: a winter coat stuffed with down feathers, or one made of woven cloth. Provide reasons to support your answer.

____

____

____

____

____

____

Name ______________________________ Date ____________

Vertebrate Animals

Section 4 Mammals

LE 5.1b: An organism's overall body plan and its environment determine the way that the organism carries out the life processes. **Also covered:** LE 4.1d, 5.1a, 5.1d, 5.1f

Skim *Section 4, then write four topics about mammals that you would like to know about.*

1. ______________________________
2. ______________________________
3. ______________________________
4. ______________________________

Review Vocabulary *Write the correct key word next to each definition.*

______________ the arrangement of the individual parts of an object that can be divided into similar parts

New Vocabulary

______________ plant-eating mammal with incisors specialized to cut vegetation and large, flat molars to grind it

______________ meat-eating animal with sharp canine teeth specialized to rip and tear flesh

______________ plant- and meat-eating animal with incisors that cut vegetables, sharp premolars that chew meat, and molars that grind food

______________ mammal whose offspring develops inside the female's uterus; has a placenta that supplies the embryo with food and oxygen and removes waste

______________ mammal that gives birth to incompletely developed young that finish developing in their mother's pouch

______________ mammal that lays eggs with tough, leathery shells instead of giving birth to live young

Academic Vocabulary *Use a dictionary to define* **complex.**

complex ______________________________

____

Main Idea | Details

Mammal Characteristics

I found this information on page ______.

Organize *7 characteristics common to mammals.*

1. ______________________________
2. ______________________________
3. ______________________________
4. ______________________________
5. ______________________________
6. ______________________________
7. ______________________________

I found this information on page ______.

Model ***and describe the different kinds of teeth carnivores, omnivores, and herbivores have. Use the figure in your book to help you.***

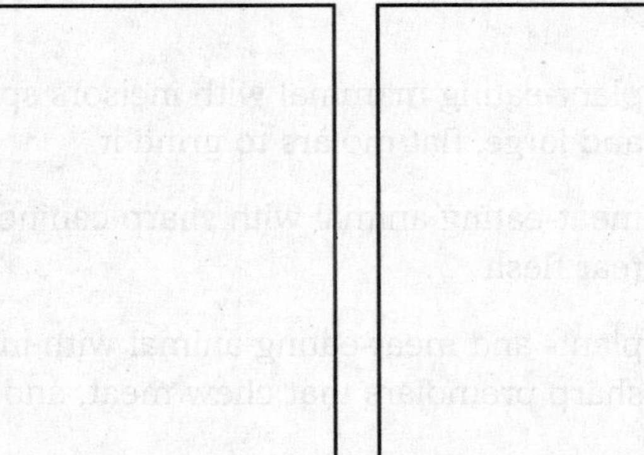

Name ______________________________ Date ______________

Section 4 Mammals (continued)

Main Idea — **Details**

Mammal Types

I found this information on page ______.

Classify *mammals by completing the following chart.*

Types of Mammals		
Type of Mammal	**Characteristics**	**Examples**
Monotreme		
Marsupial		
Placental		

CONNECT IT Choose a wild mammal that is native to your area. Classify it using the information you have learned. Provide two unique characteristics. Tell how it is adapted to its environment.

____

____

____

____

Name ______________________ Date __________

Vertebrate Animals Chapter Wrap-Up

Review the ideas you listed in the K-W-L chart at the beginning of the chapter. Cross out any incorrect information in the first column. Then complete the chart by filling in the third column.

K What I know	W What I want to find out	L What I learned

Review

Use this checklist to help you study.

- ☐ Review the information you included in your Foldable.
- ☐ Study your *Science Notebook* on this chapter.
- ☐ Study the definitions of vocabulary words.
- ☐ Review daily homework assignments.
- ☐ Re-read the chapter and review the charts, graphs, and illustrations.
- ☐ Review the Self Check at the end of each section.
- ☐ Look over the Chapter Review at the end of the chapter.

SUMMARIZE IT **After reading this chapter, identify three facts that you have learned about vertebrate animals.**

____

____

____

____

Name ______________________________ Date ______________

Plants

Before You Read

Before you read the chapter, respond to these statements.

1. Write an **A** if you agree with the statement.
2. Write a **D** if you disagree with the statement.

Before You Read	Plants
	• In tropical rain forests, there are more than 260,000 known plant species and probably more to be identified.
	• Land plants' ancestors may have been green algae that lived in the sea.
	• Ferns and mosses produce spores rather than seeds.
	• Paper and clothing are made from seed plants.

Construct the Foldable as directed at the beginning of this chapter.

Science Journal

Write three characteristics that you think all plants have in common.

Name ______________________ Date ____________

Plants

Section 1 An Overview of Plants

LE 1.1h: Living things are classified by shared characteristics on the cellular and organism level. **5.1b:** An organism's overall body plan and its environment determine the way that the organism carries out the life processes. **Also covered:** LE 1.1c, 1.1f, 3.1b, 4.1a, 4.1b, 4.3e, 5.1a, 5.1d, 5.1g, 5.2e, 6.2c

***Skim** the headings in Section 1. Then predict three facts you will learn from reading the section.*

1. ______________________
2. ______________________
3. ______________________

Review Vocabulary **Define** *the word* species. *Use your book or a dictionary for help.*

species ______________________

New Vocabulary *Use your book to define the following key terms.*

cuticle ______________________

cellulose ______________________

vascular plant ______________________

nonvascular plant ______________________

Academic Vocabulary *Use a dictionary to define* adapt *to reflect its scientific meaning.*

adapt ______________________

Name ______________________________ Date ______________

Section 1 An Overview of Plants (continued)

Main Idea | Details

What is a plant?

I found this information on page ____________.

Summarize *how plants make food by completing the concept map below. Use these terms:* photosynthesis, chlorophyll, chloroplasts.

Green plant cells

contain

[ ]

in

[ ]

that make food through the process of

[ ]

Origin and Evolution of Plants

I found this information on page ____________.

Sequence *the events in the table below. Write the oldest event at the bottom of the table and the youngest event at the top of the table.*

Events

- First cone-bearing plants
- First flowering plants
- First green algae
- First land plants

(Youngest)	
↑	
↑	
(Oldest)	

Main Idea — Details

Life on Land

I found this information on page ________.

Summarize *how land plants made life possible for land animals.*

____

____

____

Adaptations to Land

I found this information on page ________.

Identify *the four adaptations that make it possible for plants to live on land.*

Plant Adaptations to Land	
Structure	Function

Classification of Plants

I found this information on page ________.

Complete *the concept map below about plant classification.*

Classification of plants
- divides plants into two major groups called → [ ]
- was developed by → [ ]
- gives each plant species its own → [ ]

CONNECT IT Suppose that you are working at a greenhouse. While at work, a child asks you, "What's a plant?" Write a short answer to this question.

____

____

Name ______________________ **Date** ____________

Plants

Section 2 Seedless Plants

LE 5.1b: An organism's overall body plan and its environment determine the way that the organism carries out the life processes. **Also covered:** 1.1c, 4.1b, 5.1d

Skim *Section 2 of your book. Then write three questions that you have about plants. Try to answer your questions as you read.*

1. ______________________
2. ______________________
3. ______________________

Review Vocabulary

Define spore. *Use your book or a dictionary for help. Write a sentence that reflects its scientific meaning.*

spore ______________________

New Vocabulary

Use your book to define the following key terms. Then use each word in a sentence that reflects its scientific meaning.

rhizoid ______________________

pioneer species ______________________

Academic Vocabulary

Use a dictionary to define soil. *Write a sentence that reflects its scientific meaning.*

soil ______________________

Main Idea | **Details**

Seedless Nonvascular Plants

I found this information on page ________.

Organize *the characteristics of* seedless nonvascular plants *by completing the chart below.*

Characteristics of Seedless Nonvascular Plants	
1.	
2.	
3.	
4.	
5.	
6.	
7.	
8.	

I found this information on page ________.

Complete *the concept map to identify examples and characteristics of seedless nonvascular plants. One example has been listed for you.*

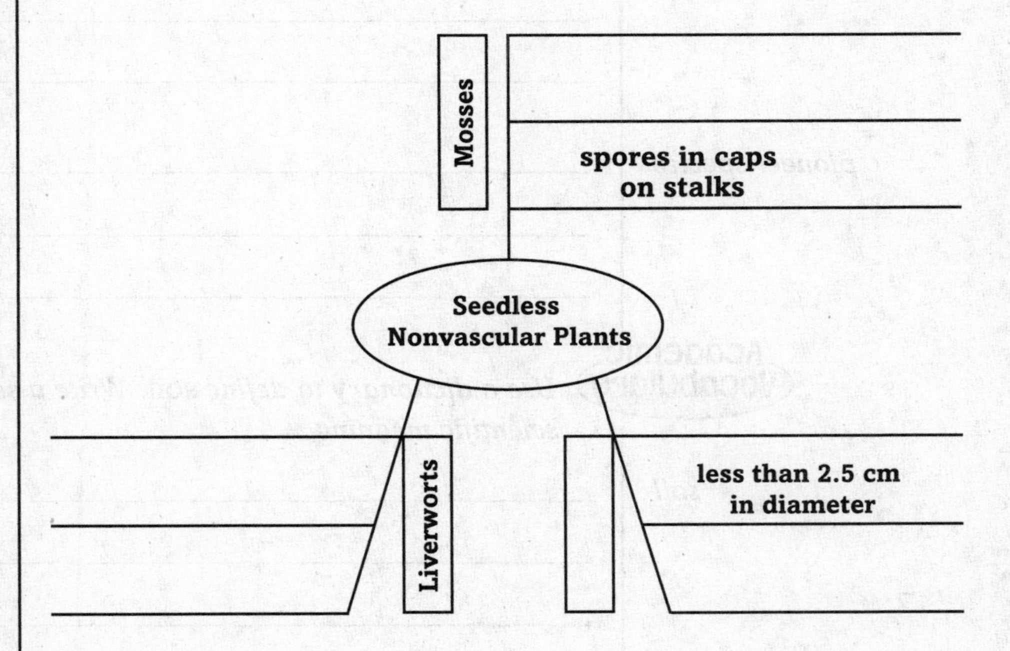

Name ______________________________ Date ____________

Main Idea **Details**

Seedless Vascular Plants

I found this information on page ________.

Compare and contrast seedless vascular plants *with* seedless nonvascular plants *in the Venn diagram below.*

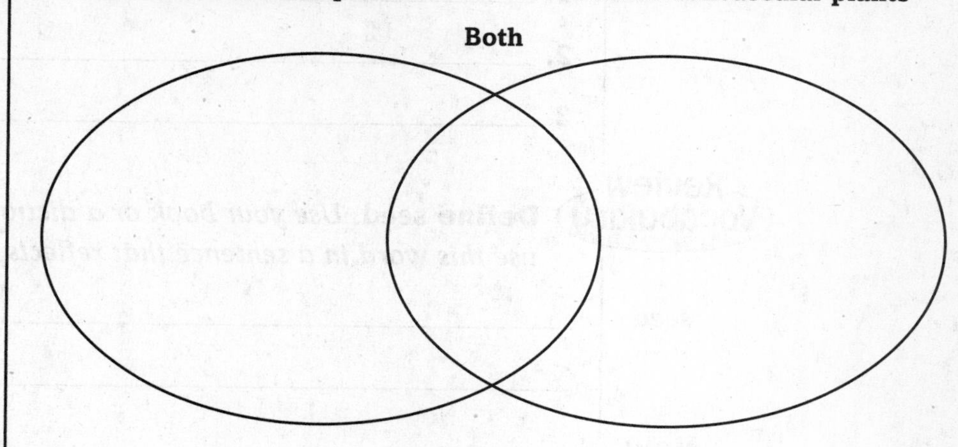

Importance of Seedless Plants

I found this information on page ________.

Summarize *the importance of seedless plants in the table below.*

Importance of Seedless Plants	
1.	
2.	
3.	
4.	
5.	
6.	
7.	

CONNECT IT Suppose you are a naturalist working in a forest area that has recently burned in a forest fire. Summarize what you would tell visitors about seedless plants and how important they are to the forest's recovery.

____

____

____

Name ______________________ Date ____________

Plants

Section 3 Seed Plants

LE 5.1b: An organism's overall body plan and its environment determine the way that the organism carries out the life processes. **Also covered:** 1.1c, 5.1d

Scan *Section 3 of your book. Write three questions that come to mind as you read the headings and examine the illustrations.*

1. ______________________
2. ______________________
3. ______________________

Review Vocabulary

Define seed. *Use your book or a dictionary for help. Then use this word in a sentence that reflects its scientific meaning.*

seed ______________________

____

New Vocabulary

Read the definitions below. Write the correct key term on the blank in the left column. Use your book for help.

______________ a vascular plant that produces seeds that are not protected by fruit

______________ a vascular plant that flowers and produces fruit with one or more seeds

______________ a plant with one cotyledon inside its seeds

______________ a plant with two cotyledons inside its seeds

Academic Vocabulary

Use a dictionary to define annual *as it applies to the length of a plant's life.*

annual ______________________

____

Name ______________________________ Date ____________

Main Idea | **Details**

Characteristics of Seed Plants

I found this information on page ______.

Create *a cross-section of a* leaf *in the space below. Label and describe the purpose of six important features.*

I found this information on page ______.

Organize *the characteristics of* seed plants *by completing the chart below.*

Structure	Function
Leaves	
Stems	
Roots	
Vascular tissue	

Name ______________________________ Date __________

Main Idea — **Details**

Gymnosperms

I found this information on page ______.

Complete *the chart below about* gymnosperms *by writing about the characteristic listed in that cell.*

Gymnosperms	
Divisions	Seeds
Flowers	Leaves

Angiosperms

I found this information on page ______.

Complete *the chart below about* angiosperms *by writing about the characteristic listed in that cell.*

Angiosperms	
Division	Seeds
Flowers	Fruits

Importance of Seed Plants

I found this information on page ______.

Skim *your book for two uses each of* gymnosperms *and* angiosperms.

Gymnosperms:

1. ______________________________

2. ______________________________

Angiosperms:

1. ______________________________

2. ______________________________

Name ______________________________ Date ______________

Tie It Together

Synthesize

In the space below, draw a sketch of a tree. Label the tree's roots, trunk, and leaves. Next to each label, write the important functions that each of these structures performs. Beneath your sketch, explain why trees are an important part of the environment.

Name ______________________________ Date ____________

Plants Chapter Wrap-Up

Now that you have read the chapter, think about what you have learned and complete the table below. Compare your previous answers with these.

1. Write an **A** if you agree with the statement.
2. Write a **D** if you disagree with the statement.

Plants	After You Read
• In tropical rain forests, there are more than 260,000 known plant species and probably more to be identified.	
• Land plants' ancestors may have been green algae that lived in the sea.	
• Ferns and mosses produce spores rather than seeds.	
• Paper and clothing are made from seed plants.	

Review

Use this checklist to help you study.

- ☐ Review the information you included in your Foldable.
- ☐ Study your *Science Notebook* on this chapter.
- ☐ Study the definitions of vocabulary words.
- ☐ Review daily homework assignments.
- ☐ Re-read the chapter and review the charts, graphs, and illustrations.
- ☐ Review the Self Check at the end of each section.
- ☐ Look over the Chapter Review at the end of the chapter.

SUMMARIZE IT

After reading this chapter, identify three things that you have learned about plants.

____

____

____

____

Name ______________________________ Date ____________

Plant Processes

Before You Read

Before you read the chapter, respond to these statements.

1. Write an **A** if you agree with the statement.
2. Write a **D** if you disagree with the statement.

Before You Read	Plant Processes
	• Plants make their own food.
	• Plants break down food to release energy.
	• Plant stems grow away from light.
	• Plants have hormones that control changes in their growth.

Construct the Foldable as directed at the beginning of this chapter.

Science Journal

Describe what would happen to life on Earth if all the green plants disappeared.

Name ______________________ **Date** ____________

Plant Processes

Section 1 Photosynthesis and Respiration

LE 5.1c: All organisms require energy to survive. Some cells use oxygen to release the energy stored in food. **6.2a:** Photosynthesis is carried on by green plants and other organisms containing chlorophyll. **Also covered:** LE 5.1b, 6.2b, 6.2c

Scan *the illustrations in Section 1. Write three questions that you have about plants. Try to answer your questions as you read.*

1. ______________________
2. ______________________
3. ______________________

Review Vocabulary

Define cellulose *using your book. Then write a sentence to illustrate its scientific meaning.*

cellulose ______________________

New Vocabulary

Use your book to define the following terms.

stomata ______________________

chlorophyll ______________________

photosynthesis ______________________

respiration ______________________

Academic Vocabulary

Use a dictionary to define release.

release ______________________

Main Idea | **Details**

Taking In Raw Materials

I found this information on page ________.

Organize *what you know about the different layers of a plant's leaves by completing the table below.*

Structure	Function
Epidermis	
Palisade layer	
Spongy layer	

I found this information on page ________.

Summarize *why* stomata *are important structures in a plant leaf.*

____

____

____

The Food-Making Process

I found this information on page ________.

Complete *the equation for* photosynthesis. *Identify:*

- the product that is stored as a food source
- the product that is released mostly as waste
- the product made during light-dependent reactions
- the product made during light-independent reactions

$6CO_2$ + $6H_2O$ + light energy → ________ + ________

carbon dioxide | **water**

Food source: ________

made during ________ ________ ________

Waste product: ________

made during ________ ________ ________

Name ______________________ Date __________

Main Idea — Details

The Breakdown of Food

I found this information on page ______.

Define aerobic respiration.

____

Complete *the equation for aerobic respiration.*

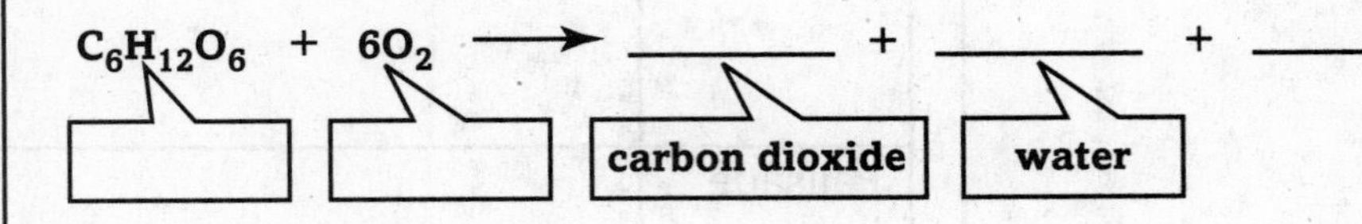

Comparison of Photosynthesis and Respiration

I found this information on page ______.

Compare *the processes of photosynthesis and aerobic respiration by completing the table.*

	Photosynthesis	Aerobic Respiration
Energy		
Raw materials		
End products		
Cell structure in which process occurs		

SUMMARIZE IT Create a concept map or other diagram to summarize what you learned in this section about plant structure and function.

Name ______________________ Date ____________

Plant Processes

Section 2 Plant Responses

LE 5.1a: Animals and plants have a great variety of body plans and internal structures that contribute to their ability to maintain a balanced condition. **Also covered:** LE 5.1b, 5.1g

Scan *Section 2. Predict three things that you will learn.*

1. ______________________
2. ______________________
3. ______________________

Review Vocabulary **Define** behavior *using your book.*

behavior ______________________

New Vocabulary *Write the correct vocabulary term next to each definition. Use your book to help you.*

______ response of a plant to external stimuli, movement caused by change in growth

______ type of plant hormone that causes plant stems and leaves to exhibit positive responses to light

______ plant's response to the number of hours of daylight and darkness it receives

______ plant that generally requires short nights—less than 12 hours of darkness—to begin the flowering process

______ plant that generally requires long nights—12 or more hours of darkness—to begin the flowering process

______ plant that does not require a specific photoperiod and can begin the flowering process over a range of night lengths

Academic Vocabulary *Use a dictionary to define* **involve.**

involve ______________________

Main Idea | **Details**

What are plant responses?

I found this information on page ______.

Distinguish *the types of stimuli as internal or external.*

______ **1.** a stimulus that comes from outside the body

______ **2.** a stimulus that comes from inside the body

Tropisms

I found this information on page ______.

Complete *the table below. Identify the stimulus for each described response.*

Stimulus	Response
	Plant stem grows faster on one side. Stem bends and twists around object.
	Plant bends toward light. Leaves turn and absorb more light.
	Roots grow downward. Stems grow upward.

Plant Hormones

I found this information on page ______.

Compare *the effects of different hormones that affect plants.*

Plant hormones

Ethylene		Gibberellins	Cytokinins	
helps	causes	stimulate	stimulate	prevents
	stems to grow toward light			seeds sprouting and buds from developing in winter, and tomatoes opening on hot days

Name ______________________________ Date ____________

Main Idea | **Details**

Plant Hormones

I found this information on page ______.

Create *a diagram to illustrate how auxin causes a stem to grow in response to sunlight. Write a short caption to describe where* auxin *is concentrated in the stem.*

Photoperiods

I found this information on page ______.

Complete *the table below to show your understanding of the effects of* photoperiodism *on different types of plants.*

Type of Plant	Hours of Darkness Needed to Flower	Examples
	need less than 12 hours	spinach, lettuce, and beets
	need 12 or more hours	poinsettias, strawberries, and ragweed
	do not need a specific amount of light	dandelions and roses

CONNECT IT **Explain plant responses you might see in plants that are growing indoors on a windowsill.**

____

____

____

Name ______________________________ Date ____________

Plant Processes Chapter Wrap-Up

Now that you have read the chapter, think about what you have learned and complete the table below. Compare your previous answers with these.

1. Write an **A** if you agree with the statement.
2. Write a **D** if you disagree with the statement.

Plant Processes	After You Read
• Plants make their own food.	
• Plants break down food to release energy.	
• Plant stems grow away from light.	
• Plants have hormones that control changes in their growth.	

Review

Use this checklist to help you study.

- ☐ Review the information you included in your Foldable.
- ☐ Study your *Science Notebook* on this chapter.
- ☐ Study the definitions of vocabulary words.
- ☐ Review daily homework assignments.
- ☐ Re-read the chapter and review the charts, graphs, and illustrations.
- ☐ Review the Self Check at the end of each section.
- ☐ Look over the Chapter Review at the end of the chapter.

SUMMARIZE IT **After reading this chapter, identify three things that you have learned about plant processes.**

____

____

____

____

Name ________________________________ Date ____________

Bacteria, Protists, and Fungi

Before You Read

Before you read the chapter, respond to these statements.

1. Write an **A** if you agree with the statement.
2. Write a **D** if you disagree with the statement.

Before You Read	Bacteria, Protists, and Fungi
	• Bacteria are one-celled organisms.
	• A healthy person should not have any bacteria living in or on their body.
	• Algae or their products are ingredients in toothpaste and ice cream.
	• Fungi break down organic materials, including food scraps and dead plants.

Construct the Foldable as directed at the beginning of this chapter.

Science Journal

Scientists have discovered some organisms are only one-celled and others are made up of many cells. List possible functions of these organisms in a pond environment.

____

____

____

____

____

Name ______________________ Date __________

Bacteria, Protists, and Fungi

Section 1 Bacteria

LE 1.1d: Some organisms are single cells; others, including humans, are multicellular. **5.1d:** The methods for obtaining nutrients vary among organisms. **Also covered:** LE 1.1c, 1.2j, 5.1e, 6.1a, 6.2c

Scan *the headings in Section 1 of your book. Identify 5 topics that will be discussed.*

1. ______________________
2. ______________________
3. ______________________
4. ______________________
5. ______________________

Review Vocabulary

disease

Use disease *in a sentence that shows its scientific meaning.*

____

____

New Vocabulary

Read the definitions below. Write each key term on the blank in the left column.

__________ any organism that uses dead material as a food and energy source

__________ any organism that causes disease

__________ a chemical that limits the growth of or kills other bacteria

__________ a dormant form of a bacterium

__________ a preparation that can help prevent disease that is made from particles taken from killed bacteria

__________ a process that is used to kill most harmful bacteria in a food product

Academic Vocabulary

internal

Use a dictionary to define internal.

____

____

Main Idea | **Details**

Characteristics of Bacteria

I found this information on page ________.

Compare and contrast *the ways that bacteria obtain food.*

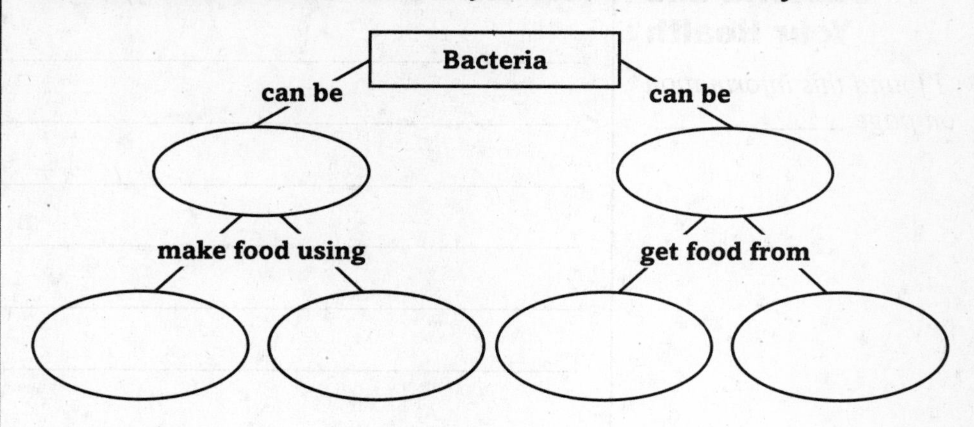

I found this information on page ________.

Model *Draw the three shapes of bacteria. Identify the shape and the special name of each one. Use the figure in your book to help you.*

Types of Bacteria

I found this information on page ________.

Compare *how the two main groups of bacteria are classified.*

How Bacteria Are Classified	
Eubacteria	Archaebacteria

Name ______________________ Date ____________

Main Idea	Details
Bacteria and Your Health *I found this information on page ______.*	**Summarize** *how bacteria can affect your health.*
Bacteria and the Environment *I found this information on page ______.*	**Sequence** *events to describe the role of nitrogen-fixing bacteria in a food chain.*

Nitrogen Fixation in the Food Chain	
1.	
2.	
3.	

SYNTHESIZE IT

Write a short paragraph about how your view of bacteria has changed as a result of reading this section.

Name ______________________ Date ____________

Bacteria, Protists, and Fungi

Section 2 Protists

LE 5.1b: An organism's overall body plan and its environment determine the way that the organism carries out the life processes. **Also covered:** LE 1.1d, 4.1a, 5.1d, 5.1e

Scan *the section headings. Then predict what you will learn in this section.*

1. ______________________

2. ______________________

3. ______________________

Review Vocabulary *Use your book or a dictionary to define* parasites.

parasites ______________________

New Vocabulary *Use your book or a dictionary to define the key terms.*

protist ______________________

protozoan ______________________

pseudopod ______________________

algae ______________________

Academic Vocabulary *Use a dictionary to define* sphere.

sphere ______________________

Name ______________________________ Date ____________

Main Idea / Details

What is a protist?

I found this information on page ______.

Compare and Contrast *protists with bacteria. Write* yes *if the type of organism has the characteristics described below. Write* no *if it does not.*

Differences Between Protists and Bacteria		
Characteristic	Protists	Bacteria
Contain a nucleus		
Have a cell membrane		
Some are made up of many cells		

I found this information on page ______.

Compare and contrast *the three protist groups by inserting each characteristic listed below within the Venn diagram.*

- are algae
- consumers
- contain chlorophyll
- eukaryotic
- grouped by how they move
- include water molds
- live in wet surroundings
- producers
- saprophytes or parasites
- some have pseudopods

Protists

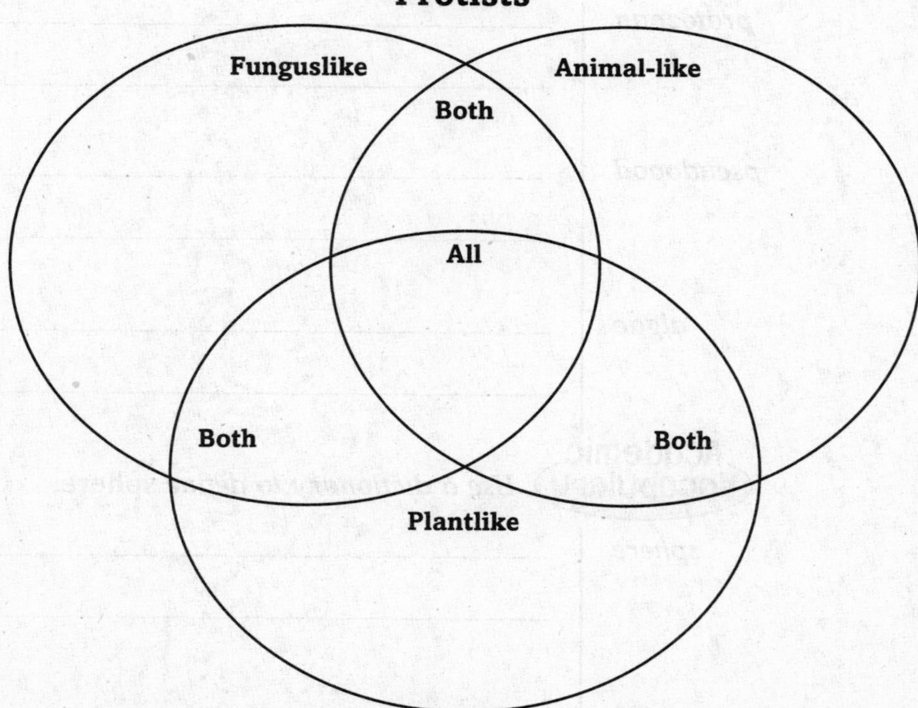

Name ______________________________ Date ____________

Main Idea — Details

The Importance of Protists

I found this information on page ________.

Organize *information about ways humans use protists such as algae. List three products in which algae are used.*

1. ______________________________
2. ______________________________
3. ______________________________

I found this information on page ________.

Summarize *malaria and the Irish potato famine on the lines below.*

Malaria: ______________________________

____

____

____

____

Irish potato famine: ______________________________

____

____

____

____

Connect It

Summarize different types and characteristics of protists.

____

____

____

____

____

Name ______________________ Date ____________

Bacteria, Protists, and Fungi

Section 3 Fungi

LE 5.1b: An organism's overall body plan and its environment determine the way that the organism carries out the life processes. **Also covered:** LE 1.1c, 4.1a, 5.1e

Scan *Section 3 of your book. Write three facts that you discovered about fungi as you scanned the section.*

1. ______________________
2. ______________________
3. ______________________

Review Vocabulary

Use producer *in a sentence that shows its scientific meaning.*

producer ______________________

New Vocabulary

Define *the following key terms.*

hyphae ______________________

sporangia ______________________

lichen ______________________

mycorrhizae ______________________

Academic Vocabulary

Use a dictionary to define accumulate. *Then use this term in a sentence that shows its scientific meaning.*

accumulate ______________________

Name ______________________________ Date ______________

Main Idea | **Details**

What Are Fungi?

I found this information on page ______________.

Organize *information about fungi by completing the sentences below.*

1. Most fungi are ______________ and ______________.
2. Like plant cells, fungus cells have ______________.
3. Most fungi are ______________, but some are ______________.
4. Fungi reproduce through the production of ______________.
5. Fungi grow best in ______________.

I found this information on page ______________.

Summarize *the structure and function of fungi by filling in the blanks.*

Hyphae are ______________ tubes. The body of a fungus is usually ______________. Cells in the hyphae ______________ food. Sexual reproduction occurs when ______________________________ ______________________________. A special structure results in which ______________ are produced.

Types of Fungi

I found this information on page ______________.

Classify *fungi by completing the graphic organizer below.*

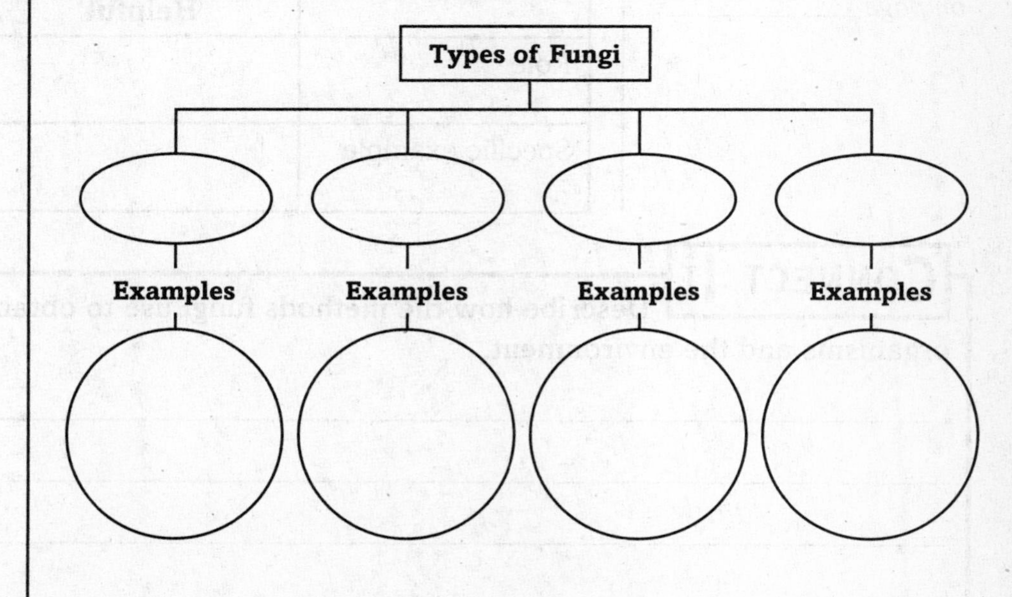

Main Idea	Details
Fungi in the Environment *I found this information on page* ______.	**Create** *a sketch to show how mycorrhizae interact with plants. Describe the role of these fungi in words under your diagram.*
Fungi and Humans *I found this information on page* ______.	**Distinguish** *ways that fungi can be helpful or harmful to humans. Give a specific example of each.*

	Helpful	Harmful
Role		
Specific example		

CONNECT IT Describe how the methods fungi use to obtain food can help other organisms and the environment.

Name ______________________ Date __________

Tie It Together

Design an Experiment

As you have learned, yeast is used to make bread. Design an experiment that involves the effect that yeast has on the production of bread. (You do not need to perform the experiment.) Your design should include these items:

- the question that you are attempting to answer by doing the experiment
- a hypothesis that you will test
- the procedure or the steps that should be followed
- the type of data you would collect
- how you will analyze the data to draw a conclusion

Question: ______________________

____

Hypothesis: ______________________

____

Procedure: ______________________

____

____

____

____

Data: ______________________

____

____

Analyzing Data: ______________________

____

____

Name ______________________________ Date __________

Bacteria, Protists, and Fungi

Now that you have read the chapter, think about what you have learned. Compare your previous answers to these.

1. Write an **A** if you agree with the statement.
2. Write a **D** if you disagree with the statement.

Bacteria, Protists, and Fungi	After You Read
• Bacteria are one-celled organisms.	
• A healthy person should not have any bacteria living in or on their body.	
• Algae or their products are ingredients in toothpaste and ice cream.	
• Fungi break down organic materials, including food scraps and dead plants.	

Review

Use this checklist to help you study.

☐ Review the information you included in your Foldable.

☐ Study your *Science Notebook* on this chapter.

☐ Study the definitions of vocabulary words.

☐ Review daily homework assignments.

☐ Re-read the chapter and review the charts, graphs, and illustrations.

☐ Review the Self Check at the end of each section.

☐ Look over the Chapter Review at the end of the chapter.

SUMMARIZE IT **After reading this chapter, list three things that you have learned about bacteria, protists, and fungi.**

____

____

____